100
best
gluten-free
foods

100
best
gluten-free
foods

**Your essential guide
to gluten-free eating with
100 tasty recipes**

This edition published by Parragon Books Ltd in 2014
LOVE FOOD is an imprint of Parragon Books Ltd

Parragon Books Ltd
Chartist House
15–17 Trim Street
Bath BA1 1HA, UK
www.parragon.com/lovefood

ISBN 978-1-4723-5468-6

Printed in China

Created and produced by made-to-measure-books
New photography by Clive Streeter
Nutritional consultant: Judith Wills

Nutritional data obtained from the USDA national nutrient database.

Notes for the Reader

This book uses both metric and imperial measurements. Follow the same units of measurement throughout; do not mix metric and imperial. All spoon measurements are level: teaspoons are assumed to be 5 ml, and tablespoons are assumed to be 15 ml. Unless otherwise stated, milk is assumed to be full fat, eggs and individual vegetables are medium, and pepper is freshly ground black pepper. Unless otherwise stated, all root vegetables should be peeled prior to using.

Garnishes, decorations and serving suggestions are all optional and not necessarily included in the recipe ingredients or method. The times given are an approximate guide only. Preparation times differ according to the techniques used by different people and the cooking times may also vary from those given. Optional ingredients, variations or serving suggestions have not been included in the time calculations.

While the author has made all reasonable efforts to ensure that the information contained in this book is accurate and up to date at the time of publication, anyone reading this book should note the following important points:-

Medical and pharmaceutical knowledge is constantly changing and the author and the publisher cannot and do not guarantee the accuracy or appropriateness of the contents of this book;
In any event, this book is not intended to be, and should not be relied upon, as a substitute for appropriate, tailored professional advice. Both the author and the publisher strongly recommend that a doctor or other healthcare professional is consulted before embarking on major dietary changes;
For the reasons set out above, and to the fullest extent permitted by law, the author and publisher: (i) cannot and do not accept any legal duty of care or responsibility in relation to the accuracy or appropriateness of the contents of this book, even where expressed as 'advice' or using other words to this effect; and (ii) disclaim any liability, loss, damage or risk that may be claimed or incurred as a consequence – directly or indirectly – of the use and/or application of any of the contents of this book.

CONTENTS

INTRODUCTION

Coeliac disease – an autoimmune disease that causes the body to produce antibodies to react to gluten – affects around one in 100 people throughout the world. The only cure is to avoid gluten completely. For life. Gluten is one of the proteins found in wheat, barley and rye, and is also in many processed foods but, thankfully, there is no need to feel deprived when you are on a gluten-free diet. With a little know-how you can have a varied, nutritionally balanced and enjoyable diet.

Coeliac disease damages the small intestine and can result in unpleasant symptoms such as nausea, bloating/wind, diarrhoea and constipation which can be very debilitating. The resulting damage to the intestine causes malabsorption of nutrients leading to other symptoms such as tiredness, headaches, mouth ulcers, hair loss, anaemia, osteoporosis and weight loss so it is important that it is properly diagnosed. Anyone recently diagnosed with coeliac disease needs as nutritious and beneficial a diet as possible as they may have suffered with poor nutrient absorption for some time.

Some people who don't have coeliac disease also follow a gluten-free diet and the number of those wishing to cut gluten from their diet is increasing. These people may suffer from bloating, wind, indigestion and irritable bowel syndrome, for example, and feel a gluten-free diet helps minimize these symptoms. Or it may be a personal choice as they may simply feel more healthy on a gluten-free diet.

As well as in wheat, barley and rye, gluten is also found in many processed foods that contain small amounts of these grains and their by-products. Some people are also sensitive to avenin, a protein similar to gluten found in oats. Many oats may also be contaminated with gluten as they are packaged in the same factories as wheat, barley or rye and so most coeliacs avoid oats too. Look out for oats labelled as gluten-free if you still wish to include them in your diet.

Foods to avoid on a gluten-free diet

The most obvious foods that may contain gluten are breads, crackers, breakfast cereals, pasta, flour, pastry, cakes and biscuits. All those not labelled as gluten-free need to be avoided by coeliacs. Many other foods contain wheat, rye or barley in smaller amounts, for example, breaded and battered fish and nuggets, drinks such as beer, desserts, confectionery, packet and tinned soups and stocks. This isn't a comprehensive list and for more information every supermarket and/or your country's coeliac organization (such as Coeliac UK) can give you details of foods that contain gluten and those that are gluten-free.

Food choices on a gluten-free diet

There are many choices of grains and 'pseudo grains' that do not contain gluten and many of these, such as quinoa, teff, amaranth, rice and buckwheat, are actually richer in health-protecting and health-promoting nutrients.

As well as these great gluten-free grains, there is also a wide choice of other naturally gluten-free foods to provide carbs in your diet. Pulses (beans, lentils and split peas) are rich in starch and come with higher levels of many of the vitamins and minerals, too. Several vegetables are high-carb – for example, sweet potatoes, parsnips and beetroot – and these also offer additional health benefits as most are rich in phytochemicals. Research into these plant chemicals shows that they are important in helping to prevent our most prevalent diseases and many of the health problems associated with ageing. Other vegetables and some fruits are also useful sources of carbohydrates, so there is plenty of choice.

There is much benefit in choosing a diet that is basically natural, rather than highly processed. The natural foods highlighted in this book don't come with long ingredients lists that you need to check for gluten, and are likely to be more nutritious. However, supermarkets are stocking more and more 'free-from' foods and often have plenty of gluten-free items. Gluten-free pastas, breads, crackers and cereals can add variety and convenience to your diet.

Get plenty of vitamins and minerals

There are several key nutrients that people following a gluten-free diet often lack: Vitamins A, B1, B2, niacin, folate, B12, D, E and K and the minerals calcium, iron, magnesium, phosphorous and zinc.

By choosing a wide range of foods from this book to eat regularly, you will almost certainly get your recommended daily allowances of vitamins and minerals, as well as all the other nutrients and compounds we need for health. For example, a mix of gluten-free grains and pulses will provide carbs, protein, folate and magnesium in abundance; fruit and vegetables are packed with phytochemicals, potassium and vitamin C and leafy greens are rich in vitamin K. Nuts and seeds are rich in unsaturated fats and zinc, while meat provides high-quality protein, iron, phosphorous and B vitamins. From eggs we get vitamins A, D and E; from fish and shellfish selenium and omega-3 fats; and from yogurt and cheese, calcium. And of course, all these foods contain many other nutrients, too.

Using this book

Within these pages you will find detailed advice about which foods to choose to boost your intake of any particular nutrient. When a food is a particularly good source of that nutrient, we've highlighted it and you'll also find a list of the major nutrients that each food contains.

We have paid particular attention to foods that help promote digestive health. Some, such as cannellini beans, bananas and pears, are particularly suitable for a sensitive gut and can help reduce bloating, improve the gut flora and help with conditions such as irritable bowel syndrome. Many foods here also offer protection against colon and bowel cancers.

We've come up with 100 great gluten-free recipes and ideas here for how to use our top 100 foods, but we are all individuals, all different, and there is no one diet that is the 'perfect' diet. As long as you get a good variety and range of foods, simply choose the foods you enjoy.

Healthy eating tips

Here are a few healthy eating tips that will help you get the best out of your gluten-free diet.

• Try to eat at least five portions a day of vegetables and fruit. (Starchy root vegetables, such as potatoes, don't count.) Try to have at least one portion a day of a leafy green vegetable and one of mixed salad.

• Aim to have at least as many vegetable portions a day as you do fruit (don't have all your five just as fruit).

• Choose a selection of different-coloured fruits and vegetables to ensure you get a wide selection of plant chemicals.

• Try to eat around three servings of a carb-rich food (e.g. rice, corn, sweet potatoes, gluten-free bread) each day.

• Have around three servings a day of a high-protein food (e.g. lean meat, fish, shellfish, hard cheese, tofu, lentils, nuts, pulses, yogurt).

• Choose foods rich in healthy fats (e.g. olive oil, nuts, salmon, pumpkin seeds) every day.

• For digestive health – and more pleasure when eating – try to eat regularly, chew food thoroughly and relax while you eat. Little and often may also be a good mantra.

GLOSSARY

ALA Alpha-linolenic acid, one of the essential fatty acids we need in small, regular amounts as it can't be produced in the body, is one of the omega-3 group of polyunsaturated fats. ALA can be converted into DHA and EPA (see opposite) by our bodies.

Amino acids The 22 'building blocks' of protein which are contained in many foods in varying combinations and amounts. Eight of these are essential (9 for children) as they can't be made from other foodstuffs in the diet.

Anti-inflammatory Having the ability to reduce inflammation in the body. Many immune system disorders, including coeliac disease, result in abnormal inflammation. Rheumatoid arthritis is an inflammatory disease, but heart disease, asthma and other conditions may all have inflammation as a factor.

Antioxidants Substances, such as some vitamins and minerals and many phytochemicals, that protect the body against the effects of free radicals, toxins and pollutants by helping to prevent oxidization in foods and in the body. Oxidization is believed to damage body cells and is linked with disease and ageing.

Blood lipids Various types of fats found in the bloodstream, sometimes binding with proteins to make, for example, LDL and HDL (see opposite). High levels in the blood – or an imbalance in the types – can be a risk factor for cardiovascular and other diseases.

Cholesterol A fatty substance in many foods such as meat, fish and dairy produce, and also manufactured in the liver, cholesterol is essential to the body but may also be an important risk factor in cardiovascular disease. (Also see HDL and LDL.)

Complete protein A food which contains the eight essential amino acids in ideal amounts. Essential amino acids are vital to help maintain and build muscle, for cell maintenance and repair and many other body functions.

DHA and **EPA** Docosahexaenoic acid and eicosapentaenoic acid are both 'long chain' omega-3 fatty acids found only in the fatty tissues in fish. They appear to help reduce the risk of cardiovascular disease and high blood pressure.

Fatty acids The components of the types of fat in our food, there are 25 fatty acid types, most of which can be made in the body. Two, the essential fatty acids linoleic acid (one of the omega-6 group) and alpha-linolenic acid (one of the omega-3 group), cannot and must be provided through diet.

Flavonoids A group of several thousand antioxidant compounds found in fruits, vegetables and other plant foods.

Free radicals Highly reactive, unstable atoms or molecules in the body which are a normal by-product of metabolism but which may, in excess, be a trigger factor for disease and ageing.

Glycaemic Index A system of ranking carbohydrate foods according to their effect on blood sugar levels. A rank of 100 is the highest – glucose (the pure form of sugar) is 100 and reaches the bloodstream very quickly. People with insulin resistance and type 2 diabetes are advised to follow a low Glycaemic Index (low GI) diet.

HDL High-density lipoproteins (a mixture of fatty cholesterol and proteins) travel through the blood, helping to remove harmful LDL cholesterol and keep arteries clear, reducing the risk of cardiovascular disease.

Homocysteine An amino acid produced by the body. High levels can damage the artery linings and make it hard for blood to clot properly, increasing the risk of heart disease and strokes.

Insoluble fibre Consisting mainly of cellulose, this type of dietary fibre is found in many plant foods – grains and vegetables are particularly good sources. It helps to keep the digestive system working properly with regular bowel movements.

Insulin A hormone produced in the pancreas which controls the amount of glucose in the blood and helps the body use it for energy. People with type 2 diabetes (the most common type) may not produce enough insulin or may be resistant to the hormone.

LDL Low-density lipoproteins are microscopic particles of protein which transport cholesterol in the blood. High levels are linked with the formation of plaques, narrowing of the arteries and coronary artery disease.

Phytochemicals Chemicals and compounds found in foods that can have many positive effects on health and disease prevention. Vegetables, fruits, grains and pulses are our major sources.

Polyphenols A group of anti-oxidant plant chemicals found in many plant foods, with a proven effect in reducing the risk of some cancers and heart disease.

Prebiotics Indigestible carbohydrates, found in foods such as onions and asparagus, which help promote the growth of 'friendly' bacteria in the gut.

Probiotics These are 'friendly' gut bacteria, such as *acidophilus* and *bifidobacteria*, found in foods like bio yogurt and miso, which help boost the immune system and have other health benefits.

Pseudo grains Starchy carbohydrate foods which are usually classified within the grain group of foods but are not true grains – they may be a fruit (e.g. buckwheat) or a seed (e.g. quinoa).

Soluble fibre A type of dietary fibre which, with water, turns to gel during digestion and helps slow down the rate at which it travels through the gut. It may help ease digestive disorders and lower cholesterol. Some grains, nuts, seeds and some fruits are particularly good sources.

Trans fats Most trans fats have been hardened from oils into solid fats in a process called hydrogenation, and have been much used in mass food production. They raise LDL and lower HDL cholesterol. Some foods, such as lamb and full-fat dairy, contain small amounts of trans fats naturally.

Grains and flours

A gluten-free diet doesn't mean that you need to miss out on healthy and versatile grains. Although some of the most commonly used grains do contain gluten, there is a very good range of grains and pseudo grains that can replace them perfectly. Most are nutritionally superior as well – many are rich in high-quality protein, as well as carbohydrate, and contain an excellent range of minerals and health-protecting plant chemicals.

(C) High in carbohydrate

(F) Very good source of fibre

(V) Rich in vitamins and minerals

(D) Particularly good for digestive health

(P) High in protein

(N) Nutrient boost for gluten-free diet

01

AMARANTH

These tiny seeds are high in protein and carbohydrate and very rich in a wide range of vitamins and minerals.

Along with quinoa, amaranth seeds are one of the few plant foods to contain all the essential amino acids in a good balance making them a valuable source of high-quality protein and a useful grain substitute for gluten-free eating. Their generous B-vitamin and mineral content increases their nutritional value. They are very high in oxygen-transporting iron – an average 60-g/2¼-oz portion will give you a third of your RDA – and contain half your RDA of magnesium, which boosts heart and bone health. Studies have shown amaranth has a powerful cholesterol-lowering effect and the choline in the seeds is known to remove harmful homocysteine (associated with heart disease) from the blood.

- A good source of high-quality protein.
- High carbohydrate content ideal for the gluten-free diet.
- Rich in several of the B vitamins including choline.
- Lowers cholesterol.

Practical tips:
Cook seeds in 2½ times their weight of water for up to 30 minutes, or until the water is absorbed. Sprinkle the cooked grains into salads and on vegetables, stir into soup or serve as a side dish. They also make a delicious porridge and can even be popped like corn. Add nutty-flavoured amaranth flour to a gluten-free mixed flour for breads, pancakes and muffins.

DID YOU KNOW?

The leaves of the amaranth plant are eaten as a vegetable in Mexico and Central and South American countries where it is native.

NUTRIENTS PER AVERAGE PORTION (60 G/2¼ OZ DRY WEIGHT) AMARANTH SEED

Calories	223
Protein	8 g
Fat	4.2 g
Carbohydrate	39 g
Fibre	4 g
Vitamin B5	0.9 g
Vitamin B6	0.3 g
Choline	42 mg
Folate	49 mcg
Calcium	95 mg
Iron	4.6 mg
Magnesium	149 mg
Phosphorous	334 mg
Potassium	305 mg
Selenium	11.2 mcg
Zinc	1.7 mg

Chilli and amaranth cornbread

MAKES 1 LOAF

2–3 fresh red chillies, or to taste
90 g/3¼ oz amaranth flour
100 g/3½ oz gluten-free white
    flour mixture
115 g/4 oz coarse polenta
    (cornmeal)
1 tbsp gluten-free
    baking powder
1 tsp gluten-free
    bicarbonate of soda
1½ tsp salt
50 g/1¾ oz sugar
125 g/4½ oz Cheddar cheese,
    coarsely grated
3 eggs
225 ml/8 fl oz buttermilk
70 g/2½ oz butter, melted and
    cooled slightly, plus extra
    for greasing
60 g/2¼ oz fresh or frozen
    sweetcorn kernels,
    thawed if frozen

Method

1 Preheat the oven to 200°C/400°F/Gas Mark 6. Preheat the grill. Grease a 900-g/2-lb loaf tin.

2 Place the chillies under the preheated grill and cook, turning occasionally, for 5–7 minutes, until blackened all over. Remove the skins and seeds and finely chop the flesh.

3 Sift together the amaranth flour, white flour mixture, polenta, baking powder, bicarbonate of soda and salt into a large bowl. Stir in the sugar and cheese.

4 Whisk the eggs with the buttermilk and melted butter until well blended.

5 Make a well in the centre of the flour mixture and pour in the egg mixture. Combine with a fork, gradually drawing in the dry ingredients from the side.

6 Stir in the chillies and sweetcorn and spoon the batter into the prepared tin, levelling the surface. Bake in the preheated oven for 40–45 minutes, until a skewer inserted into the centre comes out clean.

7 Leave to cool in the tin for 10 minutes, then turn out onto a wire rack and leave to cool completely.

02 BUCKWHEAT

One of the most nutrient-rich grains available, buckwheat has been linked with many health benefits. The nutty, rich taste lends itself to many uses.

Buckwheat isn't a true cereal but it can be used in a similar way to wheat. Regular consumption can lower total cholesterol and LDL cholesterol, and it can improve blood flow to the heart. This may be due to its high content of the blood-pressure lowering mineral potassium and its massive magnesium content (many gluten-free diets are low in magnesium). Because of its relatively high fibre, and high-quality protein content, it's also a great grain for diabetics, lowering both insulin response and blood sugars.

- Rich in many heart and circulation-friendly vitamins, minerals and plant compounds.
- Regular consumption lowers risk of diabetes and insulin resistance.
- Contains a high level of zinc, for a carbohydrate, which is important for a healthy immune system.
- A very good source of vitamins B2 and niacin, both of which can be in shortfall on a gluten-free diet.

Practical tips:
Cook buckwheat like rice to accompany casseroles and curries; add to soups and stews; or cool and use in salads to boost the protein content. Buckwheat flour makes great pancakes for breakfast and is the traditional flour used in blinis and soba noodles. The flour is also good in cake and bread flours, while buckwheat flakes make a very tasty addition to a home-made muesli.

DID YOU KNOW?

Buckwheat is the fruit seed of a plant which is related to rhubarb and sorrel, and was widely cultivated in China over 1,000 years ago.

NUTRIENTS PER AVERAGE PORTION (60 G/2¼ OZ DRY WEIGHT) BUCKWHEAT

Calories	206
Protein	7.9 g
Fat	2 g
Carbohydrate	42.9 g
Fibre	6 g
Vitamin B2	0.26 mg
Vitamin B5	0.7 g
Folate	18 mcg
Niacin	4.2 mg
Iron	1.3 mg
Magnesium	139 mg
Potassium	276 mg
Selenium	11.2 mcg
Zinc	1.4 mg

Golden pilaf

SERVES 4

450 ml/15 fl oz gluten-free
    vegetable or chicken stock
200 g/7 oz toasted buckwheat
3 tbsp olive oil
1 onion, thinly sliced
2 garlic cloves,
    thinly sliced
2-cm/¾-inch piece fresh ginger,
    thinly sliced
½ tsp ground turmeric
½ tsp ground cinnamon
4 tbsp orange juice
85 g/3 oz sultanas
2 carrots, coarsely grated
55 g/2 oz pine nuts, toasted
salt and pepper
fresh coriander, to garnish

Method

1 Bring the stock to the boil in a large pan and add the buckwheat. Simmer for 5–6 minutes until most of the liquid is absorbed, then add 1 tablespoon of the oil, cover and leave on a low heat for 10 minutes, until tender.

2 Heat the remaining oil in a large frying pan and fry the onion over a medium heat for 5–6 minutes, stirring occasionally, until soft and golden brown.

3 Add the garlic and ginger and stir for 1 minute, then stir in the turmeric, cinnamon, orange juice and sultanas and cook for 1 minute. Add the carrots, cooked buckwheat and pine nuts, stirring until evenly heated. Season to taste with salt and pepper.

4 Pile the pilaf onto a warm serving plate and garnish with coriander.

03

CORN

One of the most popular starchy foods across the Western world, bright yellow and naturally sweet, corn is an ideal and adaptable cereal for any gluten-free diet.

Corn not only tastes good, it also contains a wide variety of antioxidant chemicals including the carotenes lutein and zeaxanthin (vital for good vision) and other carotenes that our bodies convert to vitamin A, deficient in many people following a gluten-free diet. Another antioxidant in corn is coumarin for cancer prevention, a healthy vascular system and lower blood pressure. Corn is a good source of choline, a member of the B-vitamin group (which helps to regulate fat metabolism, supports the liver, brain function and nervous system and is an anti-inflammatory) and also of vitamin B5 pantothenic acid which helps release energy from sugars, starches and fats.

- Rich in carotenes, including lutein and zeaxanthin, for eye health.
- Contains coumarin for cancer prevention and vascular health.
- High in potassium and antioxidants to control blood pressure.
- Fresh corn is a useful source of vitamin C.

Practical tips:
Eat fresh or frozen corn kernels or cobs for the highest levels of B and C vitamins. Polenta is an Italian dish made with cornmeal (dried and ground corn) boiled into a creamy porridge – ideal as a side dish for meat, chicken or other main dishes. Use coarse cornmeal to coat fish or chicken before baking or frying, or to make cornbread or corn fritters. Cornflour is generally used as a thickener for sauces or as a bulking agent and has little nutritional value.

DID YOU KNOW?

Another name for corn – a staple food in South America and Africa – is maize. Both corn and maize refer to the grass classified as *Zea mays*.

NUTRIENTS PER 100 G/3½ oz FRESH RAW CORN KERNELS

Calories	88
Protein	3 g
Fat	0.8 g
Carbohydrate	20.7 g
Fibre	2.1 g
Vitamin B5	0.4 g
Choline	24 mg
Folate	36 mg
Niacin	1.7 mg
Vitamin C	6.4 mg
Magnesium	18 mg
Potassium	213 mg

Vegetable tart with a polenta crust

SERVES 4

*olive oil, for greasing and
 brushing*
850 ml/1½ pints boiling water
250 g/9 oz quick-cook polenta
*1 tbsp chopped fresh oregano,
 plus extra to garnish*
*1 small yellow pepper, deseeded
 and thinly sliced*
1 small red onion, thinly sliced
1 small courgette, thinly sliced
2 tomatoes, sliced
*100 g/3½ oz mozzarella cheese,
 diced*
8 black olives, stoned and halved
salt and pepper

Method

1 Preheat the oven to 200°C/400°F/Gas Mark 6. Grease a large baking sheet. Pour the water into a large pan, add a pinch of salt, and bring to the boil over a high heat. Add the polenta in a steady stream, stirring continuously until smooth.

2 Reduce the heat and stir constantly for 4–5 minutes, or until the polenta is thick and smooth. Remove from the heat and stir in the oregano. Season to taste with pepper. Spoon the polenta onto the prepared baking sheet and spread out in a 30-cm/12-inch round, raising the edges slightly.

3 Arrange the pepper, onion, courgette and tomatoes over the polenta and add the mozzarella. Top the tart with the olives and brush lightly with olive oil.

4 Bake in the preheated oven for 15–20 minutes, or until bubbling and golden brown. Garnish with oregano and serve immediately.

04

MILLET

Tiny millet grains are very versatile and pack a nutritional punch. They contain several nutrients that can be in short supply on a gluten-free diet.

Millet is particularly high in phosphorous – one of the nutrients highlighted as being in potential shortfall on a gluten-free diet. It plays an important role in bone and nervous system maintenance, energy conversion from food and in fat metabolism. An average 60-g/2¼-oz portion of millet will give you around a fifth of your daily needs. Millet is also a very good source of magnesium and B vitamins, which can be low in a gluten-free diet. Magnesium is essential for heart health, while vitamin B5 helps your metabolism and folate helps proper brain function.

- Contains a good range of nutrients known to be low in the average gluten-free diet.
- Rich in phosphorous for bone health and fat metabolism.
- A very good source of fibre and iron.
- Contains potassium for blood pressure control and muscle function.

Practical tips:

Cook millet as you would rice – in boiling water – until tender. Use it hot as an accompaniment to meats, poultry and fish or use it cold in salads. Creamed millet, simmered in a mix of milk and water until very tender and creamy, is good with any dish in which you'd use polenta (see Corn, page 16). Add grated cheese/chopped herbs for extra flavour. Add millet flour to your bakes, including bread and muffins, or make into a flatbread.

DID YOU KNOW?

Millet was first eaten many thousands of years ago in north Africa where it is still a staple grain today.

NUTRIENTS PER AVERAGE PORTION (60 G/2¼ OZ DRY WEIGHT) MILLET

Calories	227
Protein	6.6 g
Fat	2.5 g
Carbohydrate	43.7 g
Fibre	5.1 g
Vitamin B5	2.8 g
Folate	51 mcg
Iron	1.8 mg
Magnesium	68 mg
Phosphorous	171 mg
Potassium	213 mg

Salmon parcels with millet and spinach

SERVES 4

150 g/5½ oz millet, rinsed
4 salmon fillets, each about
175 g/6 oz and 3 cm/
1¼ inches thick
15-cm/6-inch piece leek,
cut into matchsticks
1 carrot, cut into matchsticks
1 celery stick, cut into
matchsticks
1 tbsp snipped fresh chives
85 g/3 oz butter
200 g/7 oz baby spinach
salt and pepper

Method

1 Preheat the oven to 220°C/425°F/Gas Mark 7 and place a baking tray inside. Cut out four 33-cm/13-inch squares of greaseproof paper.

2 Bring a saucepan of water to the boil. Add the millet and ½ teaspoon of salt. Bring back to the boil, then reduce the heat and simmer briskly for 10 minutes. Drain and set aside.

3 Place a salmon fillet in the centre of each greaseproof paper square. Arrange the leek, carrot and celery on top and sprinkle with the chives. Season to taste with salt and pepper and dot with half the butter. Roll up the edges of the paper securely, leaving room in the parcel for steam to circulate.

4 Place the parcels on the preheated baking tray and bake in the preheated oven for 12 minutes.

5 Meanwhile, heat the remaining butter in a frying pan over a medium–high heat. Stir in the cooked millet and the spinach and heat until the spinach has just wilted. Season to taste with salt and pepper.

6 Divide the millet and spinach between four plates and transfer the contents of one of the parcels on top of each. Serve immediately.

05

QUINOA

This little pseudo grain from South America is a perfect food to include on a gluten-free diet as it has a superb nutritional profile and a great flavour.

Quinoa is one of the few 'complete protein' plant foods meaning it contains all nine essential amino acids. It's a particularly good plant source of lysine which helps us absorb calcium and make hormones. Calcium is especially concentrated in quinoa – it contains over twice the amount found in wheat. The seeds are rich in antioxidant compounds including immune-boosting quercetin and anti-inflammatory kaempferol. Unlike other grain foods, quinoa is a good source of healthy fats. A quarter is oleic acid (a heart-healthy fat) and it also contains alpha-linolenic acid (ALA), the omega-3 fat that can help reduce high cholesterol and blood pressure. Quinoa is also one of the easiest grains to digest making it particularly useful for anyone with digestive problems.

- A complete source of protein.
- A useful source of calcium, antioxidants and healthy fats.
- A very good source of potassium, iron, magnesium and zinc.
- A good source of the B vitamin group, especially folate and B1.

Practical tips:
Boil quinoa seeds in water until tender. For a nuttier flavour, dry roast or dry-pan fry for 5 minutes before boiling. Combine cooked, chilled quinoa with chopped vegetables, salads, beans and herbs or spices for a healthy meal. Use instead of wheat in tabbouleh. You can buy quinoa noodles and flour as a healthy substitute for wheat grains in your bakes. Quinoa is easy to sprout or puff (follow instructions given on packaging) or buy ready sprouted or puffed.

DID YOU KNOW?

Quinoa is not a cereal grain (a grass) at all, but the seed of a member of the beet family. Along with amaranth and buckwheat, it is sometimes termed a 'pseudo cereal' – a product that looks like and can replace a true cereal in the diet.

NUTRIENTS PER AVERAGE PORTION (60 G/2¼ oz DRY WEIGHT) QUINOA

Calories	221
Protein	8.5 g
Fat	3.6 g
Carbohydrate	38.5 g
Fibre	4.2 g
Vitamin B1	0.2 g
Folate	110 mcg
Calcium	28 mg
Iron	2.7 mg
Magnesium	118 mg
Potassium	338 mg
Zinc	1.8 mg

Fruity puffed quinoa

SERVES 1

25 g/1 oz puffed quinoa
125 ml/4 fl oz apple juice
1 small banana, thinly sliced
½ crisp, red-skinned apple,
    sliced into thin segments
2 tsp pumpkin seeds
honey, for drizzling
Greek yogurt, to serve (optional)

Method

1 Put the puffed quinoa into a serving bowl. Stir in the apple juice, making sure the puffs are submerged. Leave to stand for a few minutes.

2 Arrange the banana slices and apple segments on top of the quinoa.

3 Scatter over the pumpkin seeds and drizzle with a little honey. Serve immediately with yogurt, if using.

06

TEFF

One of the grains highest in protein, teff is also rich in minerals and contains a type of starchy fibre that is very good for your digestive health.

Teff ranks with quinoa and amaranth in its high protein content, though it isn't regarded as a complete protein. It is very high in bone-building calcium and in iron to help beat fatigue and for healthy blood. Perhaps most interesting is the fibre found in teff. Around 30% of teff's fibre is resistant starch, a relatively recently-researched type of fibre which is helpful for diabetics, people with insulin resistance and for anyone trying to lose weight as it helps control insulin and blood sugar levels and keeps hunger at bay for longer. Teff is also the ideal grain for colon health – resistant starch produces a substance called butyrate in the colon which is associated with a reduced risk of colon diseases, including cancer.

- One of the grains highest in protein.
- Rich in calcium and iron.
- High in resistant starch to help maintain blood sugar levels and a healthy colon.
- High levels of potassium to help regulate blood pressure.

Practical tips:
Traditionally teff is ground into flour and used to make a spongy flatbread called *injera*. Try it as a single flour or mix with other gluten-free flours for pancakes, biscuits and wraps. Ivory-coloured teff has the mildest flavour; darker varieties have a stronger taste. Simmer the grains in water, as you would rice, and add to soups and stews.

DID YOU KNOW?

Tiny teff seeds have long been grown in Ethiopia and can grow in very cold and wet areas where other grains don't thrive. The famed long-distance runners of Ethiopia eat teff for its ability to provide long-term energy.

NUTRIENTS PER AVERAGE PORTION (60 G/2¼ oz DRY WEIGHT) TEFF

Calories	220
Protein	8 g
Fat	1.4 g
Carbohydrate	44 g
Fibre	4.8 g
Vitamin B5	0.6 mg
Vitamin B6	0.3 mg
Niacin	2 mg
Calcium	108 mg
Iron	4.6 mg
Magnesium	110 mg
Potassium	256 mg
Zinc	2.2 mg

Chocolate and ginger cookies

MAKES 12

75 g/2¾ oz wholemeal teff flour

25 g/1 oz gluten-free plain flour

1½ heaped tsp gluten-free
   cocoa powder

1 heaped tsp ground ginger

½ tsp gluten-free baking powder

75 g/2¾ oz soft light brown
   sugar

60 g/2¼ oz butter, at room
   temperature

1 large egg, beaten

30 g/1 oz gluten-free dark
   chocolate, chopped

30 g/1 oz stem ginger in syrup,
   drained and chopped

2 tsp ginger syrup

Method

1 Preheat the oven to 180°C/350°F/Gas Mark 4 and line a baking tray with baking parchment. Place the flours, cocoa powder, ginger and baking powder in a mixing bowl and combine thoroughly with a fork.

2 In another bowl, beat together the sugar and butter with a wooden spoon until pale and creamy – if the butter is soft it is quick and easy to do this. Add the egg little by little and beat until combined. Add a spoonful of the flour mixture if it looks like curdling.

3 Tip in the remaining flour mix and combine with the wooden spoon. Stir in the chocolate, stem ginger pieces and the ginger syrup. Use a tablespoon to drop 12 spoonfuls of the mixture onto the prepared baking tray, leaving plenty of space between each as the cookies will spread. Place the tray in the preheated oven and bake for 12 minutes.

4 Remove from the oven and use a flat spatula to transfer to a wire rack to cool completely.

07 SORGHUM

Sorghum, a grain that has been cultivated for thousands of years, is a rich source of several health-promoting plant chemicals.

It is only in recent years that the health benefits of sorghum have been researched and it seems this grain has big potential to protect us from many diseases. It is rich in phytochemicals including tannins, phenolic acids, anthocyanins, phytosterols and policosanols. Policosanols are thought to be as effective as statins in lowering cholesterol, while a compound in sorghum called 3-DXA appears to stop the spread of colon cancer cells. Sorghum also contains antioxidant phenols linked with a reduction in the complications both of insulin resistance and diabetes, while the grain's tannins are said to reduce calorie absorption. And as sorghum is a low-GI food it may be useful for anyone watching their weight.

- Rich in plant chemicals linked with a variety of health benefits.
- High in a compound very effective at reducing cholesterol.
- May be helpful to those watching their weight.

Practical tips:
Use sorghum in various dishes instead of rice, and cook it in a similar way. Try it in a tabbouleh with fresh herbs. You can also pop sorghum grains as you would corn for a healthy snack – try them sprinkled with paprika. Sorghum flour (the wholegrain version contains most nutrients) has a mild flavour and is excellent added to any gluten-free mixed grain flour for baking as it can help improve the texture.

DID YOU KNOW?

Sorghum is the fifth most important cereal in the world, first harvested 8,000 years ago in Egypt but not arriving in the USA until the nineteenth century.

NUTRIENTS PER AVERAGE PORTION (60 g/2¼ oz RAW WEIGHT) SORGHUM

Calories	203
Protein	6.8 g
Fat	2 g
Carbohydrate	44.8 g
Fibre	3.8 g
Niacin	1.8 mg
Calcium	17 mg
Iron	2.6 mg
Magnesium	166 mg
Potassium	210 mg
Zinc	2 mg

Seven grain bread

MAKES 1 LOAF

butter, for greasing
60 g/2¼ oz amaranth flour
*120 g/4¼ oz brown
rice flour*
120 g/4¼ oz sorghum flour
60 g/2¼ oz cornflour
60 g/2¼ oz tapioca flour
*20 g/¾ oz ground
chia seeds*
*100 g/3½ oz ground
flaxseeds*
2 tsp xanthan gum
*2 tsp easy-blend
dried yeast*
1 tsp salt
3 eggs
1 tbsp vegetable oil
2 tbsp sugar
240 ml/8½ fl oz tepid water
10 g/¼ oz sunflower seeds

Method

1 Grease a 450-g/1-lb loaf tin.
2 Combine the flours, chia seeds, flaxseeds, xanthan gum, yeast and salt together in a bowl.
3 In a separate bowl, mix the eggs, oil, sugar and water together until well combined. Add the dry ingredients to the egg mixture and mix to form a soft dough.
4 Put the dough into the prepared tin, sprinkle with the sunflower seeds and cover with a clean damp tea towel for 1 hour or until the dough rises. Preheat the oven to 180°C/350°F/Gas Mark 4.
5 Bake the loaf in the preheated oven for 40–45 minutes, until golden brown. Cool in the tin for 5 minutes, then turn out onto a wire rack to cool completely.

08

GRAM FLOUR

High in protein and with a broad range of important nutrients for the gluten-free diet, gram flour should definitely have a place in your kitchen.

Gram flour has been a staple food in India and the Middle East for many years, prized for its high protein (double that of wheat), carbohydrate content and its many minerals. Made from chickpeas, it has a similar nutritional profile and is an ideal addition to a gluten-free diet. It is one of the plant foods highest both in folate and choline, two B vitamins that reduce levels of harmful homocysteine, (an amino acid thought to promote cardiovascular disease by damaging blood vessels and making blood more likely to clot) in the blood. It is also rich in magnesium, which can be low in a gluten-free diet. Deficiency can have a negative effect on the heart, blood pressure, bones, insulin function, sleep patterns and general health so this flour is extremely beneficial.

- A high-protein, nutritious alternative to many more commonly used flours.
- Rich in folate and choline.
- Great source of magnesium.
- Contains many nutrients that may be lacking on a gluten-free diet.

Practical tips:

Gram flour, with its slightly nutty flavour, is traditionally used to make pakoras, poppadums and bhajis. It is a high-protein alternative to wheat in many other recipes including pancake batters, breads and sauces, and can be used as an egg-replacer in many baking recipes (beat together 3 tablespoons of gram flour with 3 tablespoons of water to replace each egg).

DID YOU KNOW?

Gram flour is made from ground roasted chickpeas. Besan flour is made from raw chickpeas and has a sharper flavour.

NUTRIENTS PER 100 G/3½ oz GRAM FLOUR

Calories	387
Protein	22 g
Fat	6 g
Carbohydrate	57 g
Fibre	10 g
Choline	95 mg
Folate	437 mcg
Niacin	1 mg
Vitamin E	0.5 mg
Calcium	45 mg
Iron	4 mg
Magnesium	166 mg
Potassium	846 mg
Zinc	2 mg

Spiced gram flour rolls

MAKES 24

vegetable or groundnut oil,
*   for greasing*
250 g/9 oz gram flour, sifted
100 g/3½ oz set natural yogurt
600 ml/1 pint warm water
2 tsp salt
¼ tsp ground turmeric
2 tsp grated fresh ginger
2 garlic cloves, crushed
4 tsp green chilli paste

Topping

6 tbsp vegetable or groundnut oil
1 tsp sesame seeds
1 tsp black mustard seeds
4 tbsp finely chopped fresh
*   coriander*
2 tbsp freshly grated coconut

Method

1 Lightly brush four large baking trays with oil and set aside.

2 Place the gram flour, yogurt and water in a heavy-based saucepan with the salt, turmeric, ginger, garlic and green chilli paste. Whisk until smooth, then place over a medium heat and continue to whisk constantly. When the batter starts to thicken (after about 5–6 minutes), reduce the heat to low, cover and cook for 4–5 minutes. Stir, re-cover and cook for a further 2–3 minutes, or until thickened and smooth.

3 Remove from the heat and ladle the batter onto the prepared baking trays, using a palette knife to spread the mixture as thinly as possible. The batter will start to set as it cools. Leave to stand for 5 minutes, then slice it lengthways into 5-cm/2-inch wide strips. This quantity should make about 24 rolls.

4 Starting at one end of each strip, use the palette knife to gently lift and roll (like a small Swiss roll). Repeat until all the strips have been rolled. Transfer to a serving plate.

5 Meanwhile, make the topping. Heat the oil in a frying pan and add the sesame seeds and mustard seeds. When they start to pop, remove from the heat and drizzle this spiced oil over the gram flour rolls. Sprinkle over the coriander and coconut. Serve warm or at room temperature.

09

SAGO

The small balls, or pearls, of sago are noteworthy for their very high carbohydrate, low-fibre content and are very easy to digest.

Traditionally, sago was considered an ideal food for infants and people who were ill, convalescing or elderly, as it is a particularly easy-to-digest food – very high in pure carbohydrate with virtually no fibre, protein or fat content. The pearls are also a useful food for anyone suffering from digestive problems associated with food allergies and anyone wanting to put on weight. In traditional herbal medicine sago was recommended as a treatment for heat/acidity in the digestive system – today interpreted as indigestion. The pearls do contain a small amount of iron and a very little calcium.

- Very high in easily-digested carbohydrate.
- A food almost anyone can eat without fear of allergy or an intolerant reaction.
- Small iron and calcium content.
- Useful for anyone wishing to gain weight.

Practical tips:

Sago pearls can be boiled with water or milk and sugar to make a sweet, cold dessert or hot pudding. When they are cooked the 'grains' become translucent. In India sago is often fried in oil with onion, spices, herbs and coconut and served as a savoury grain. Use sago flour to lighten gluten-free mixed baking flours for biscuits, cakes, pancakes and sponges.

DID YOU KNOW?

Sago, originating from New Guinea, is obtained from the stems of the sago palm tree and processed into balls. Sago and tapioca are not from the same plant although they look and taste similar.

NUTRIENTS PER AVERAGE PORTION (60 G/2¼ oz DRY WEIGHT) SAGO PEARLS

Calories	212
Protein	Trace
Fat	0.5 g
Carbohydrate	56 g
Fibre	0.3 g
Calcium	6 mg
Iron	0.7 mg

Blueberry and lime sago dessert

SERVES 4 ⒸⒹ

300 ml/10 fl oz coconut milk
300 ml/10 fl oz water
75 g/2¾ oz sago pearls
25 g/1 oz shredded coconut
40 g/1½ oz caster sugar
grated rind and juice of 1 lime
1 tsp vanilla extract
½ tsp ground cinnamon
¼ tsp grated nutmeg
20 blueberries
60 g/2¼ oz fresh mango, diced

Method

1 Bring the coconut milk and water to the boil in a saucepan over a medium heat. Pour in the sago, stirring with a fork to keep the pearls separate. Turn down the heat and simmer on very low for 20 minutes, stirring frequently to prevent the sago sticking to the pan.

2 Meanwhile, put the coconut in a non-stick frying pan over a high heat, stirring occasionally, for 1 minute, or until it turns golden. Immediately remove from the heat and set aside.

3 When the sago has simmered for 20 minutes, add the sugar, lime rind and half the juice, the vanilla extract and spices. Stir well and simmer for a further 10 minutes, or until the sago pearls are virtually transparent and tender. If the mixture becomes too thick to simmer before the sago is cooked through, add a little boiling water and mix in thoroughly. When the sago is ready, take the pan off the heat and stir in the remaining lime juice. Allow to cool for 10 minutes.

4 Spoon the sago mixture between four stemmed glasses or ramekins and smooth the top with the back of the spoon. Cover and chill for 30 minutes–1 hour. Decorate each dessert with a quarter of the toasted coconut, blueberries and diced mango.

10

TAPIOCA

Mild-tasting tapioca is rich in starch which is easy to digest and is an ideal source of carbohydrate for anyone with digestive problems.

Tapioca is an unusual food – although its pearly appearance looks somewhat like a real grain, it comes from the root of the cassava plant and is then manufactured into the small white balls. Cassava (or manioc) root is extremely high in starch and has been cooked as an important source of calories and energy for people in countries such as South America, Africa and India for centuries. Being easy to digest, it is often recommended as an ideal food to eat to gain weight and for people with digestive problems. Tapioca is not rich in vitamins or minerals but it does contain a useful amount of iron and calcium and may contain small amounts of potassium, phosphorous and magnesium.

- Very high starch, low-fat food.
- Easy to digest and low in fibre.
- Suitable for weight gain diets, especially for the elderly and those convalescing.
- Contains useful amount of calcium and iron.

Practical tips:
Tapioca pudding (made with milk, eggs, sugar and vanilla) is probably the most famous use of the pearls, certainly in the UK. Tapioca flour can be mixed half and half with rice flour to make a pancake batter or used in a gluten-free flour mix with denser flours for flatbreads and muffins. The flour is a useful gluten-free thickener for sauces and casseroles.

DID YOU KNOW?

Bubble (boba) tea, invented in Taiwan, is now a popular drink throughout Asia and also in the USA. The most basic version is simply a milky tea, often with added sugar or syrup, with large tapioca pearls in the bottom.

NUTRIENTS PER AVERAGE PORTION (60 G/2¼ oz DRY WEIGHT) TAPIOCA

Calories	215
Protein	Trace
Fat	Trace
Carbohydrate	53.2 g
Fibre	0.5 g
Calcium	12 mg
Iron	1 mg

Tapioca and potato cakes

MAKES 15–20

2 potatoes, peeled and roughly
   chopped
200 g/7 oz medium-sized
   tapioca pearls
250 ml/9 fl oz cold water
2 fresh red chillies, finely
   chopped
1 tsp cumin seeds
1 tsp salt
4 tbsp finely chopped fresh
   coriander
vegetable or groundnut oil,
   for deep-frying

Method

1 Place the potatoes in a pan of boiling water. Boil for 12–15 minutes, or until just tender. Drain thoroughly and transfer to a mixing bowl.

2 Meanwhile, place the tapioca in a bowl and pour over the water. Leave to soak for 12–15 minutes, or until the water has been absorbed and the tapioca is swollen. Transfer to a sieve to drain away any excess liquid.

3 Add the chillies, cumin seeds, salt and coriander to the potatoes and mash until fairly smooth. Stir in the soaked tapioca and mix well. With wet hands, roll the mixture into 15–20 walnut-sized balls, then flatten to make patties.

4 Heat enough oil for deep-frying in a large saucepan or deep-fryer to 180–190°C/350–375°F, or until a cube of bread browns in 30 seconds. Working in batches, deep-fry the tapioca and potato cakes for 3–4 minutes, or until golden brown. Remove with a slotted spoon and drain on kitchen paper. Serve warm.

11

BROWN RICE

Nutrient-rich brown rice is a very useful grain for a gluten-free diet as its mild flavour and good texture make it suitable for a wide range of dishes.

Rice is one of the most important grains for anyone on a gluten-free diet as its high starchy carbohydrate content is a vital source of energy. While white rice contains few nutrients, brown rice has several nutritional benefits. It's a good source of dietary fibre to help reduce cholesterol and combat heart disease and it has a lower GI than many other grains, particularly basmati. Brown rice also contains some protein and is a good source of the essential amino acids lysine and tryptophan (vital for building important proteins in the body). And it contains vitamin E and a range of B vitamins (both of which can be in shortfall in those not eating fortified wheat bread) and several minerals, including selenium and magnesium.

- Moderately low GI helps control blood sugar fluctuations.
- Good B vitamin content to convert food into energy and keep the nervous system healthy.
- Rich in the antioxidant mineral selenium which helps protect against some cancers.
- High in magnesium for a healthy heart and bone density.

Practical tips:
Brown rice is a perfect accompaniment to savoury dishes or for risottos and puddings, while rice noodles are ideal for Asian dishes and soups. Use brown rice flour to make great puddings and biscuits, and to thicken sauces in sweet and savoury dishes. Add rice flakes to muesli or use to make porridge. Rice will store in cool, dark, dry conditions in an airtight container for several months.

DID YOU KNOW?

Rice has been a staple food for half of the world's population for 6,000 years, arriving in the UK and USA only around 400 years ago.

NUTRIENTS PER AVERAGE PORTION (60 G/2¼ oz DRY WEIGHT) BROWN RICE

Calories	222
Protein	5 g
Fat	1.8 g
Carbohydrate	46 g
Fibre	3.6 g
Vitamin B1	0.2 mg
Vitamin B5	0.9 mg
Vitamin B6	0.3 mg
Niacin	3 mg
Vitamin E	0.7 mg
Calcium	20 mg
Iron	0.8 mg
Magnesium	86 mg
Selenium	19.6 mcg
Zinc	1.3 mg

Chicken and brown rice salad

SERVES 4

250 g/9 oz easy-cook brown rice
2 tsp tomato purée
500 g/1 lb 2 oz skinless chicken
   breast fillets
85 g/3 oz ready-to-eat dried
   apricots, diced
55 g/2 oz raisins
55 g/2 oz pickled lemons,
   drained and finely chopped
1 small red onion, finely
   chopped
85 g/3 oz kale, shredded
3 tbsp pine nuts, toasted

Dressing
2 tsp harissa
4 tbsp olive oil
juice of 1 lemon
salt and pepper

Method

1 Put the rice in a saucepan of boiling water. Bring back to the boil, then simmer for 25–30 minutes, or until tender. Drain, then transfer to a salad bowl.

2 Meanwhile, to make the dressing, put the harissa, oil and lemon juice in a clean jam jar, season to taste with salt and pepper, screw on the lid and shake well.

3 Spoon 2 tablespoons of the dressing into a bowl and mix in the tomato purée. Preheat the grill to high and line the grill pan with foil. Put the chicken on the foil in a single layer.

Brush some of the tomato dressing over the chicken, then grill for 15–18 minutes, or until golden and cooked through, turning the meat and brushing it with the remaining tomato dressing halfway through cooking. Cut through the middle of a breast to check that the meat is no longer pink and any juices run clear and are piping hot. Cover and leave to cool.

4 Drizzle the remaining dressing over the rice in the salad bowl. Add the dried apricots, raisins, pickled lemons and onion, then toss gently together and leave to cool.

5 Add the kale and pine nuts to the salad and stir well. When cool, thinly slice the chicken, arrange on top of the salad and serve.

12 RED RICE

Red rice makes a delicious change from brown rice in your diet and the grains contain a high level of important antioxidants called anthocyanins.

There are several varieties of red rice grown across the world with slightly differing nutritional benefits but all contain the antioxidant group anthocyanins and these give the rice its red colouring. These pigments have important health benefits – they are anti-inflammatory and can help reduce arthritis symptoms and they have anti-carcinogenic activity so can protect against cancers. They can also help prevent cardiovascular disease, promote good vision and help maintain a healthy weight and body fat percentage. Red rice has a similar vitamin and mineral profile to brown rice but it does vary depending on the specific type you use – the nutrient values given here are approximate only.

- One of the only grains high in important anthocyanins.
- Excellent for arthritis sufferers as eating it regularly can help reduce inflammation.
- Important for good vision.
- May help with weight loss and body fat reduction.

Practical tips:
Most varieties of red rice can be cooked in exactly the same way as brown rice, though some may take less time – check the instructions. Red rice makes a real visual impact on the plate and is a good accompaniment to paler foods such as white fish or chicken. It has a mild flavour and goes well with fruit and nuts in a salad. Camargue red rice is different from other varieties – it has a short grain and a nutty flavour and is excellent in risottos.

DID YOU KNOW?

One of the most highly prized types of red rice – Bhutan red rice – is grown 8,000 feet high up in the Himalayas. Irrigated with glacier water, it is said to contain more minerals than other varieties.

NUTRIENTS PER AVERAGE PORTION (60 G/2¼ oz DRY WEIGHT) RED RICE

Calories	220
Protein	4.8 g
Fat	1.8 g
Carbohydrate	45 g
Fibre	2.4 g
Calcium	20 mg
Iron	0.5 mg
Magnesium	60 mg
Phosphorous	140 mg
Potassium	108 mg
Zinc	0.9 mg

Grilled prawns with crisp-fried red rice

SERVES 4

500 g/1 lb 2 oz raw tiger prawns,
  peeled and deveined
juice of 4 limes
1 small fresh red chilli, deseeded
  and finely chopped
5 tbsp olive oil
125 g/4½ oz Camargue
  red rice, rinsed
300 ml/10 fl oz water
3 heads of red chicory,
  leaves separated
10–12 radishes, sliced
3 spring onions, sliced
4 tbsp red quinoa sprouts
salt and pepper

Method

1 Put the prawns into a shallow dish. Stir in the lime juice, chilli and 2 tablespoons of the oil. Leave to marinate in the refrigerator for 2 hours.

2 Put the rice into a saucepan with the water and ½ teaspoon of salt. Bring to the boil, then cover and simmer for 40 minutes. Fluff up with a fork and spread on a tray to dry.

3 Meanwhile, soak four wooden skewers in a shallow dish of water for at least 30 minutes. Preheat the grill.

4 Tip the rice into a frying pan large enough to spread it out in a thin layer. Place over a medium-high heat and drizzle over the remaining oil. Fry for a few minutes until a crust forms. Turn and fry for a further few minutes. Keep warm over a low heat until ready to serve.

5 Meanwhile, drain the prawns, thread onto the soaked skewers and season to taste with salt and pepper. Place under the preheated grill and cook for 5–6 minutes, until pink all over.

6 Divide the chicory between four plates and top with the rice, radishes and spring onions.

7 Remove the prawns from the skewers and arrange on top of the salad. Sprinkle with the quinoa sprouts and serve immediately.

13

WILD RICE

Wild rice – a slim, black grain that has become more widely available in recent years – is a unique food with several health benefits, especially for the heart, and a great addition to a gluten-free diet.

It contains nearly twice as much protein as brown rice and more than many other grains, so has a more beneficial effect on regulating blood sugar levels. It also contains a little more fibre and more iron – vital for transporting oxygen through our bodies and helping to prevent fatigue. The magnesium content – important for bone and heart health – is excellent. Wild rice also has 30 times more powerful antioxidant activity than white rice and can help lower total cholesterol and improve your blood lipids profile. It is a particularly good source of niacin, a B vitamin involved in the release of energy from food.

- A high-nutrient grain with many potential health benefits.
- Its high protein content makes it a useful grain for blood sugar stability and hunger prevention.
- High magnesium content for bone health.
- Several nutrients to help boost energy levels.

Practical tips:
Wild rice takes a long time to cook – up to an hour, depending on its age. With its nutty, smoky flavour, it is an ideal grain to mix with other rices or with quinoa or buckwheat, and makes a great addition to salads. Leftover wild rice freezes well in a container or robust plastic freezer bag.

DID YOU KNOW?

Wild rice is not a true rice at all, but is seed from a grass that grows in marshy areas, particularly in the USA.

NUTRIENTS PER AVERAGE PORTION (60 G/2¼ oz DRY WEIGHT) WILD RICE

Calories	214
Protein	8.8 g
Fat	0.6 g
Carbohydrate	44.5 g
Fibre	3.7 g
Vitamin B5	0.6 mg
Vitamin B6	0.2 mg
Folate	57 mcg
Niacin	4 mg
Vitamin E	0.5 mg
Iron	1.2 mg
Magnesium	106 mg
Potassium	256 mg
Zinc	3.6 mg

Bean and wild rice salad

SERVES 6

175 g/6 oz wild rice
*200 g/7 oz canned kidney beans,
    drained and rinsed*
*200 g/7 oz canned flageolet
    beans, drained and rinsed*
*200 g/7 oz canned haricot
    beans, drained and rinsed*
1 red onion, thinly sliced
4 spring onions, finely chopped
1 garlic clove, crushed

Dressing

4 tbsp olive oil
2 tbsp balsamic vinegar
1 tsp dried oregano

Method

1 Place the rice in a large saucepan, cover with water and bring to the boil. Reduce the heat then simmer for 45 minutes, or according to the instructions, until the rice is just tender and beginning to 'pop'. If necessary, add more boiling water as the rice cooks. When the rice is cooked, drain, refresh with cold water and drain again.

2 To make the dressing, combine all the ingredients in a small bowl with a fork or small whisk.

3 Place all the beans in a large salad bowl with the onion, spring onion and garlic. Add the cooled rice and pour in the dressing. Mix together thoroughly, using a wooden or metal spoon. Chill in the refrigerator before serving.

Pulses

Pulses are a double blessing for anyone on a gluten-free diet because they are rich both in carbohydrate and protein. One of them – the soya bean – is a complete protein with a perfect balance of all the essential amino acids. Pulses are rich in various types of fibre to help the digestive system and all are rich in B vitamins, antioxidant minerals and plant chemicals to support good health.

(C) High in carbohydrate

(F) Very good source of fibre

(V) Rich in vitamins and minerals

(D) Particularly good for digestive health

(P) High in protein

(N) Nutrient boost for gluten-free diet

14 ADZUKI BEANS

Adzuki beans are very high in carbohydrates and rich in dietary fibre, protein, folate and minerals, making them an ideal pulse in a gluten-free diet.

Adzukis are a tasty way for gluten-free eaters to get a perfect balance of complex carbohydrates and protein. In addition, regular consumption of these small red beans offers cardiovascular benefits in a variety of ways. They are rich in soluble fibre, which helps lower blood cholesterol levels, and they also contain excellent amounts of magnesium, potassium and folate, all of which support heart and arterial health. Adzuki beans are rich in vitamin B1, essential for metabolizing carbs into energy and to support nerve, muscle and heart function.

- Perfect balance of carbohydrates and protein.
- Several heart-friendly nutrients and soluble fibre.
- Good source of vitamin B1.
- Helps boost your calcium and zinc intake.

Practical tips:
Soak dried beans for 1 hour, then bring to the boil in fresh water for 10 minutes and simmer for 45 minutes, or until tender. Drain and cool to use in a bean salad. Alternatively, soak overnight then sprout over several days, rinsing each day. These small beans are versatile and the dried beans can even be ground into a high protein flour with a sweet, nutty flavour ideal for baking cakes and cookies. In Asia, adzuki beans are often cooked to a soft consistency with coconut milk and used to add colour, flavour and protein to rice dishes.

DID YOU KNOW?

Adzukis are sometimes called red cow peas. They are a staple in Japan and China, and in traditional Chinese medicine adzukis are said to bring strength and to offer support for the kidneys and reproductive organs.

NUTRIENTS PER AVERAGE PORTION (60 G/2¼ oz DRY WEIGHT) ADZUKI BEANS

Calories	197
Protein	12 g
Fat	0.3 g
Carbohydrate	38 g
Fibre	7.6 g
Vitamin B1	0.3 mg
Vitamin B5	0.9 mg
Folate	373 mcg
Calcium	40 mg
Iron	3 mg
Magnesium	76 mg
Potassium	752 mg
Zinc	3 mg

Salsa bean dip

SERVES 4

200 g/7 oz cherry tomatoes,
   quartered
1 small red onion, very finely
   chopped
200 g/7 oz canned adzuki beans,
   drained and rinsed
½ red pepper, deseeded and
   finely chopped
½ or 1 red chilli (to taste),
   deseeded and very finely
   chopped
2 tsp sun-dried tomato purée
1 tsp agave nectar
large handful of chopped fresh
   coriander
salt and pepper
4 small soft gluten-free tortillas,
   to serve
chilli oil, to serve

Method
1 Place the tomatoes, onion, beans, red pepper, chilli, sun-dried tomato purée, agave nectar and coriander in a large bowl. Mix together well and season to taste with salt and pepper.
2 Cover the bowl and leave in the refrigerator for at least 15 minutes to let the flavours develop. Preheat the grill to medium.
3 Place the tortillas under the preheated grill and lightly toast. Leave to cool slightly then cut into slices.
4 Transfer the bean dip to a small serving bowl. Serve with the sliced tortillas and chilli oil to dip.

15 CANNELLINI BEANS

Firm-textured cannellinis are extremely rich in soluble fibre which can help calm a sensitive gut – a common problem for anyone with coeliac disease.

An average 60-g/2¼-oz serving of cannellini beans will give you more than half of your RDA for total fibre, including a rich amount of soluble fibre which can help calm a sensitive gut as it forms a gel in the digestive tract. This gel binds with cholesterol and helps remove it from our bodies, so cannellinis are also an excellent food for anyone with high cholesterol levels. The folate content helps to bring down levels of homocysteine in the blood, high amounts of which are harmful to the arteries, while magnesium and potassium help lower blood pressure. Good levels of iron help boost energy levels and lower the risk of anaemia.

- Extremely rich in fibre and soluble fibre for a healthy digestive system and protection for the heart and arteries.
- Very high folate content helps remove harmful homocysteine from the blood.
- Can help reduce high blood pressure.
- Very good source of iron.

Practical tips:
Soak dried beans overnight, then boil for 10 minutes in fresh water and simmer for 1½–2 hours, or until tender. Try them in soup or in a three-bean salad, or add them to a lamb casserole. They marry well with lemon juice, tomatoes and garlic and are used in many classic Italian dishes.

DID YOU KNOW?

Cannellini beans (closely related to haricots and kidney beans) are one of Italy's favourite pulses, particularly in Tuscany – the Tuscan white bean and vegetable soup is world-famous.

NUTRIENTS PER AVERAGE PORTION (60 G/ 2¼ OZ DRY WEIGHT) CANNELLINI BEANS

Calories	200
Protein	14.2 g
Fat	0.4 g
Carbohydrate	36 g
Fibre	14.9 g
Vitamin B1	0.3 mg
Folate	236 mcg
Calcium	86 mg
Iron	4.9 mg
Magnesium	84 mg
Potassium	844 mg
Zinc	1.7 g

White chicken chilli

SERVES 6

1 tbsp vegetable oil

1 onion, diced

2 garlic cloves, finely chopped

1 green pepper, deseeded and
  diced

1 small green jalapeño chilli,
  deseeded and diced

2 tsp chilli powder

2 tsp dried oregano

1 tsp ground cumin

1 tsp salt

500 g/1 lb 2 oz canned cannellini
  beans, drained and rinsed

750 ml/1¼ pints gluten-free
  chicken stock

450 g/1 lb cooked chicken
  breasts, shredded

juice of 1 lime

25 g/1 oz chopped fresh
  coriander

Method

1 Heat the oil in a large, heavy-based saucepan over a medium-high heat. Add the onion, garlic, green pepper and chilli and cook, stirring occasionally, for about 5 minutes, or until soft. Add the chilli powder, oregano, cumin and salt and cook, stirring, for about a further 30 seconds. Add the beans and stock and bring to the boil. Reduce the heat to medium-low and simmer gently, uncovered, for about 20 minutes.

2 Ladle about half of the bean mixture into a blender or food processor and purée. Return the purée to the pan along with the shredded chicken. Simmer for about 10 minutes, or until heated through. Just before serving, stir in the lime juice and coriander. Serve immediately.

16 BLACK BEANS

Black beans are an ideal low-cost addition to a gluten-free diet – they contain a good balance of protein and carbohydrates, and are rich in minerals and B vitamins.

Black beans' extremely high fibre content – both soluble and insoluble – means they have strong cholesterol-lowering ability. They also contain several nutrients that play a part in maintaining the cardiovascular system. Their potassium content (which can help lower high blood pressure) is extraordinarily high, while they're also rich in magnesium (linked with protection from heart disease), folate and choline (both of which reduce damaging homocysteine in the blood), and antioxidant anthocyanins (which reduce the risk of blood clots). These antioxidants may also reduce the risk of cancer and diabetes, while their prebiotic content maintains colon health.

- High fibre food to maintain colon health and reduce cholesterol.
- Several nutrients for cardiovascular health in excellent amounts.
- Rich in folate for healthy blood and development.
- An ideal balance of protein and carbohydrates.

Practical tips:
Dried black beans should be soaked for 8 hours then drained, added to fresh water, boiled for 5 minutes then simmered for around 1½ hours, or until tender. They have a slight mushroom flavour and are a tasty addition to a gluten-free diet. Try them fried and lightly crushed as a topping for baked potatoes or use them to give a Cuban twist to the classic Jamaican dish of rice and peas.

DID YOU KNOW?

A recent study found that adults who regularly eat beans weigh around 3 kg (7 lb) less than non-pulse eaters, even though they consume 200 calories a day more.

NUTRIENTS PER AVERAGE PORTION (60 G/2¼ oz DRY WEIGHT) BLACK BEANS

Calories	205
Protein	13 g
Fat	0.8 g
Carbohydrate	37.4 g
Fibre	9.1 g
Vitamin B1	0.5 mg
Choline	40 mg
Folate	266 mcg
Calcium	74 mg
Iron	3 mg
Magnesium	103 mg
Potassium	890 mg
Zinc	2 g

Black bean and quinoa burritos

MAKES 8

60 g/2¼ oz red quinoa, rinsed
150 ml/5 fl oz water
2 tbsp vegetable oil
1 red onion, diced
1 fresh green chilli,
    deseeded and diced
1 small red pepper,
    deseeded and diced
400 g/14 oz canned black
    beans, drained and rinsed
juice of 1 lime
4 tbsp chopped fresh coriander
2 tomatoes
8 gluten-free corn tortillas,
    warmed
125 g/4½ oz Cheddar cheese,
    coarsely grated
85 g/3 oz shredded cos lettuce
salt and pepper

Method

1 Put the quinoa into a saucepan with the water. Bring to the boil, then cover and simmer over a very low heat for 15 minutes. Remove from the heat, but leave the pan covered for a further 5 minutes to allow the grains to swell. Fluff up with a fork and set aside.

2 Heat the oil in a frying pan. Fry half the onion, half the chilli and all the red pepper until soft. Add the beans, cooked quinoa and half the lime juice and coriander. Fry for a few minutes, then season to taste with salt and pepper.

3 Halve the tomatoes and scoop out the seeds. Add the seeds to the bean mixture. Dice the tomato flesh and place in a bowl with the remaining coriander, onion, chilli and lime juice, and salt to taste. Stir.

4 Place 5 tablespoons of the bean mixture on top of each tortilla. Sprinkle with the tomato salsa, the cheese and lettuce. Fold the end and sides over the filling, roll up and serve immediately.

17 BLACK-EYED BEANS

Black-eyed beans rank amongst the top 40 foods rich in antioxidants, according to the US Department of Agriculture, and they are rich in many minerals, too.

These pretty beans are high in flavonoids, a group of plant chemicals which help to keep our hearts and arteries healthy and can reduce the risk of cancer and boost the immune system. With an excellent carbohydrate content they make a good alternative source of starch to gluten-free grains in the diet. The beans are some of the richest foods in potassium, a mineral that not only helps regulate blood pressure but is also important for healthy muscle function and bone strength, and in folate, for a healthy blood fats profile. Other nutrients found in black-eyed beans in good amounts are iron, zinc and calcium.

- High in a range of flavonoids for heart and artery health and to protect against disease.
- High in complex carbohydrates.
- Very high in potassium and folate.
- A useful source of minerals including iron, zinc and calcium.

Practical tips:
Soak dried black-eyed beans for 4 hours before rapidly boiling for 5 minutes, then simmer for up to 2 hours, or until tender. You can enhance the quality of the protein in the beans by serving them with wholegrain rice or quinoa. They are also a good addition to a bean burger and make a tasty salsa (mix with chopped red onion, red pepper, fresh red chilli, coriander and lime juice).

DID YOU KNOW?

Although black-eyed beans are perhaps most well-known as a 'soul food' in the southern states of the USA, they were probably first grown in West Africa and Asia, arriving in the USA in the seventeenth century.

NUTRIENTS PER AVERAGE PORTION (60 G/2¼ OZ DRY WEIGHT) BLACK-EYED BEANS

Calories	186
Protein	14 g
Fat	1 g
Carbohydrate	32.4 g
Fibre	5 g
Folate	378 mcg
Calcium	49 mg
Iron	4.6 mg
Magnesium	84 mg
Potassium	702 mg
Zinc	1.9 g

Bean and vegetable chilli

SERVES 4　

4 tbsp gluten-free vegetable
   stock
1 onion, roughly chopped
1 green pepper, deseeded and
   finely chopped
1 red pepper, deseeded and
   finely chopped
1 tsp finely chopped garlic
1 tsp finely chopped fresh ginger
2 tsp ground cumin
½ tsp chilli powder
2 tbsp tomato purée
400 g/14 oz canned chopped
   tomatoes
400 g/14 oz canned kidney
   beans, drained and rinsed
400 g/14 oz cooked black-eyed
   beans, drained and rinsed
salt and pepper
gluten-free tortilla chips, to serve

Method

1　Heat the stock in a large saucepan, add the onion and peppers and simmer for 5 minutes, or until softened.

2　Add the garlic, ginger, cumin, chilli powder, tomato purée and tomatoes and stir to combine. Season to taste with salt and pepper and simmer for 10 minutes.

3　Stir in all the beans and simmer for a further 5 minutes, or until heated through thoroughly. Serve immediately with tortilla chips.

18

BORLOTTI BEANS

Because borlottis are particularly plentiful in fibre and a low-GI food, they are excellent for regulating blood sugar levels and keeping hunger at bay.

Borlotti beans are higher in dietary fibre, both soluble and insoluble, than many other beans and are, in fact, one of the highest-fibre foods of all. Fibre can be lacking in a gluten-free diet, so it's a good idea to eat pulses, including borlotti beans, regularly. Just one 60-g/2¼-oz portion can give you around half an adult's RDA. This fibre content means that the beans are digested slowly, not provoking a sharp rise in blood sugars. They are therefore low on the Glycaemic Index, packed with slow-releasing energy and will keep you feeling fuller for longer than most other carbohydrate foods. They will also help improve your blood fats profile if eaten regularly and are high in phosphorous to help maintain strong bones and teeth.

- Very rich in soluble and insoluble fibre.
- Good food for regulating blood sugar levels and insulin secretion.
- Very high level of folate, vital for healthy pregnancy and foetus.
- Phosphorous content helps bones and teeth.

Practical tips:
Borlotti beans have a nutty flavour and are delicious added to a bean salad with cannellini beans, fresh green beans and a lemony dressing to complement the flavour. Soak dried beans overnight, then boil rapidly in fresh water for 10 minutes, drain and rinse again before placing into a pan of fresh water and simmering for 1½–2 hours, or until tender.

DID YOU KNOW?

Borlottis – sometimes nicknamed cranberry beans because the coloured markings are cranberry-red – are an important part of the Italian diet.

NUTRIENTS PER AVERAGE PORTION (60 G/2¼ oz DRY WEIGHT) BORLOTTI BEANS

Calories	201
Protein	14 g
Fat	0.5 g
Carbohydrate	36 g
Fibre	14 g
Folate	362 mcg
Calcium	76 mg
Iron	3 mg
Magnesium	94 mg
Phosphorous	223 mg
Potassium	799 mg
Selenium	8.5 mcg
Zinc	2.2 g

Borlotti bean salad with eggs

SERVES 4

*250 g/9 oz dried borlotti
    beans, soaked overnight
    or for at least 8 hours*
*2 large garlic cloves,
    crushed*
juice of 2 lemons
6 tbsp extra virgin olive oil
1 small onion, finely chopped
*2 tomatoes, deseeded and
    finely chopped*
*40 g/1½ oz fresh flat-leaf
    parsley, finely chopped*
1 tsp cumin seeds, crushed
salt and pepper

Garnish

4 eggs
1 lemon, cut into 4 wedges
*pinch of sumac or dried crushed
    red chillies*

Method

1 Drain and rinse the beans, put them in a large saucepan, cover with fresh cold water and bring to the boil. Boil rapidly for at least 10 minutes, then remove from the heat, drain and rinse again. Add fresh cold water, bring to the boil, then simmer for 1½–2 hours, or until tender, topping up with boiling water if needed. Drain and tip into a shallow serving dish.

2 For the garnish, put the eggs in a saucepan and pour in enough cold water to cover them by 1 cm/½ inch. Bring to the boil, then reduce to a simmer and cook for 8 minutes. Drain immediately, cool quickly under cold running water, then peel and cut into quarters.

3 Lightly crush some of the warm beans with the back of a spoon. Add the garlic, lemon juice, olive oil and 1 teaspoon of salt while the beans are warm, and mix together. Add the onion, tomatoes, parsley and cumin seeds, season to taste with pepper, then toss gently together. Arrange the hard-boiled eggs and lemon wedges on top, sprinkle with the sumac and serve.

19

HARICOT BEANS

High-fibre haricots are one of the best pulses for all-round good nutrient content, providing protection against several diseases and health problems.

Haricot beans are a very high fibre food, over half of which is insoluble fibre – the type that ensures regular bowel movement and is linked with protection from digestive disorders including diverticulitis and IBS, and offers protection against colon cancer. The beans are particularly high in most of the important minerals, including iron (a 60-g/2¼-oz portion gives about a quarter of your RDA), and magnesium (a third of your RDA in a portion). The same portion size provides a third of your RDA for Vitamin B1, shown to help improve digestive problems such as ulcers and poor appetite. Haricots are also high in tryptophan, the amino acid which helps the brain produce serotonin, the mood-improving chemical.

- Rich in insoluble fibre to protect from digestive disorders.
- Excellent source of iron and magnesium.
- Good source of a range of other nutrients including calcium, zinc and B1.
- High in tryptophan to boost brain production of serotonin.

Practical tips:
Soak the dry beans for 8 hours, change the water, fast boil for 5 minutes and simmer for 1½–2 hours, or until tender. Haricots are one of the mildest-flavoured pulses of all, so they are best used in soups, casseroles and composite dishes where they can soak up other flavours. They go particularly well with tomatoes, chilli, olive oil and lemon juice and with strong-tasting vegetables such as kale.

DID YOU KNOW?

Haricots, known as navy beans in the USA, are the traditional bean used in Boston baked beans and the canned baked beans popular in the UK.

NUTRIENTS PER AVERAGE PORTION (60 G/2¼ oz DRY WEIGHT) HARICOT BEANS

Calories	202
Protein	13.4 g
Fat	0.9 g
Carbohydrate	36.4 g
Fibre	14.6 g
Vitamin B1	0.5 mg
Folate	218 mcg
Calcium	88 mg
Iron	3.4 mg
Magnesium	105 mg
Potassium	711 mg
Zinc	2.1 g

Pumpkin and haricot bean soup

SERVES 4

1 tsp olive oil
1 red onion, chopped
2 garlic cloves, crushed
450 g/1 lb pumpkin, peeled,
    deseeded and chopped into
    small cubes
2 tsp smoked paprika
¼ tsp dried chilli flakes
5–6 fresh sage leaves, finely
    chopped
850 ml/1½ pints gluten-free
    vegetable stock
400 g/14 oz canned haricot
    beans, drained and rinsed
salt and pepper
handful fresh flat-leaf parsley,
    finely chopped, to garnish

Method

1 Heat the oil in a saucepan and fry the onion and garlic for
    3–4 minutes. Add the pumpkin and cook for a further 4–5 minutes.
2 Add the paprika, chilli and sage and cook for 1 minute, stirring all
    the time.
3 Pour in the stock and season to taste with salt and pepper. Cover
    and simmer for 20–25 minutes, or until the pumpkin is tender. Allow
    the soup to cool slightly then process, using a hand-held blender,
    until smooth.
4 Stir in the haricot beans and heat through for 2–3 minutes. Serve
    garnished with the parsley.

20

KIDNEY BEANS

Red kidney beans make a large starch and nutrient contribution to a gluten-free diet and are also high in plant sterols, with strong cholesterol-lowering power.

These popular beans, while not usually classified as a complete protein, contain the nine essential amino acids and are rich in complex carbohydrate so can replace grains as a gluten-free starch for your plate. Kidney beans are higher than most other natural foods in plant sterols, which help lower blood cholesterol by up to 15%. Extremely high in fibre, much of it insoluble, kidney beans can also keep your bowels regular and help protect against colon cancer. The fibre also gives the beans a low GI rating and makes them an ideal food for slimmers and diabetics. Like many pulses, kidney beans are rich in several minerals, including a quarter of your RDA for magnesium and zinc, and a third of your RDA for iron in one 60-g/2¼-oz portion.

- Inexpensive source of good quality protein.
- Rich in gluten-free starches and fibre.
- High in sterols to lower cholesterol.
- Good source of a range of important minerals.

Practical tips:
Soak dried kidney beans for 8 hours, then change the water and fast boil for at least 10 minutes to remove the toxin phytohaemagglutinin, which can cause severe illness. After boiling, simmer until cooked for 1–2 hours, or until tender. Kidney beans are a welcome addition to meat dishes, such as chilli con carne, work well in veggie burgers and make a good salad with other pulses, green beans and an oil and vinegar dressing.

DID YOU KNOW?

Store dried kidney beans and other pulses in airtight containers in a cool, dry cupboard for up to a year or even longer. The older the bean, the longer it will take to cook.

NUTRIENTS PER AVERAGE PORTION (60 G/2¼ OZ DRY WEIGHT) KIDNEY BEANS

Calories	200
Protein	14 g
Fat	0.5 g
Carbohydrate	36 g
Fibre	14.9 g
Folate	236 mcg
Niacin	1.2 mg
Thiamin (B1)	0.3 mg
Calcium	86 mg
Iron	4.9 mg
Magnesium	84 mg
Potassium	844 mg
Zinc	1.7 g

Three-bean energy-booster salad

SERVES 4

200 g/7 oz green beans,
    halved
200 g/7 oz frozen edamame
    beans or frozen broad beans
150 g/5½ oz frozen sweetcorn
400 g/14 oz canned kidney
    beans, drained and rinsed
2 tbsp chia seeds

Dressing

3 tbsp olive oil
1 tbsp red wine vinegar
1 tsp gluten-free wholegrain
    mustard
1 tsp agave syrup
4 tsp finely chopped
    fresh tarragon
salt and pepper

Method

1 Put the green beans, edamame beans and sweetcorn in a saucepan of boiling water. Bring back to the boil, then simmer for 4 minutes, until the green beans are just tender. Drain into a colander, rinse with cold water, then drain again and transfer to a salad bowl.

2 Add the kidney beans and chia seeds to the bowl and toss gently to mix together.

3 To make the dressing, put the oil, vinegar and mustard in a clean jam jar, then add the agave syrup and tarragon and season to taste with salt and pepper. Screw on the lid and shake well. Drizzle over the salad, toss gently together and serve immediately.

21 PINTO BEANS

These attractive beans with dark red markings are crammed with vitamins and minerals, particularly magnesium, potassium and folate.

NUTRIENTS PER AVERAGE PORTION (60 G/2¼ oz DRY WEIGHT) PINTO BEANS

Calories	208
Protein	12.8 g
Fat	0.7 g
Carbohydrate	37.5 g
Fibre	9.3 g
Vitamin B1	0.4 mg
Vitamin B5	0.5 g
Vitamin B6	0.3 g
Choline	39.7 mg
Folate	315 mcg
Niacin	0.7 mg
Calcium	68 mg
Iron	3 mg
Magnesium	106 mg
Phosphorous	247 mg
Potassium	836 mg
Zinc	1.4 mg

Like all pulses, pintos are high in fibre with all the health benefits that brings and are a particularly good food to add to a gluten-free diet as they are a valuable source of starch. However, it is their excellent range and amount of minerals that makes them such a healthy food. They contain more magnesium than most other pulses – this mineral is not only vital for helping to control blood pressure but also helps maintain healthy nerves, bones and muscles, and is an immune-booster. It also helps the body utilise the energy in foods and regulates blood sugar levels. Pinto beans also contain very good amounts of B vitamins, including choline for a healthy liver and to remove harmful homocysteine from the blood.

- Valuable source of starchy, high fibre carbohydrate for those on a gluten-free diet.
- Very high in magnesium with its range of health benefits.
- Rich in several other minerals and B vitamins.
- Contains choline for healthy liver and blood.

Practical tips:
Soak dried pinto beans for 8 hours, then change the water and fast boil for 10 minutes. Change the water then simmer for 1½ hours, or until tender. Pintos have a pleasant, creamy texture and look very attractive. Use in place of red kidney beans in a chilli con carne or in a three-bean salad. Seasoned, puréed beans make a good filling for baked potatoes or sandwiches.

Country-style pinto beans with ham

SERVES 4

2 tbsp olive oil

1 large onion, chopped

2 green peppers, deseeded and chopped

4 garlic cloves, crushed

1 tsp ground cumin

500 g/1 lb 2 oz cooked pinto beans

3 tbsp tomato ketchup

25 g/1 oz molasses sugar or soft dark brown sugar

2 tbsp cider vinegar

2 tsp gluten-free Worcestershire sauce

2 tsp gluten-free French mustard

150 ml/5 fl oz gluten-free vegetable or chicken stock

250 g/9 oz cubed cooked ham

salt and pepper

2 tbsp chopped fresh flat-leaf parsley, to serve

cooked brown rice, to serve

Method

1 Heat the oil in a flameproof casserole set over a medium-low heat, add the onion and peppers and cook for 5 minutes, stirring occasionally. Add the garlic and cumin, stir to combine and cook for a further minute.

2 Stir in the beans, ketchup, sugar, vinegar, Worcestershire sauce, mustard, stock and ham, combining everything well. Bring to a simmer, cover with a lid and cook gently for 45 minutes.

3 Season with salt and pepper to taste and sprinkle over the parsley. Serve with brown rice.

22

CHICKPEAS

Chickpeas are a high-fibre source of complex carbs and protein, and have a strongly beneficial effect on blood fats, the digestive system and insulin.

DID YOU KNOW?

One of the most popular ways to eat chickpeas is as hummus, the nutrient-rich dip originating in countries such as Morocco and Turkey, and made with tahini (sesame seed paste), garlic and olive oil.

NUTRIENTS PER AVERAGE PORTION (60 G/2¼ oz DRY WEIGHT) CHICKPEAS

Calories	218
Protein	11.6 g
Fat	3.6 g
Carbohydrate	36.4 g
Fibre	10.4 g
Vitamin A	12 mcg
Vitamin B1	0.3 mg
Vitamin B5	1 g
Vitamin B6	0.3 g
Choline	57 mg
Folate	334 mcg
Niacin	0.9 mg
Vitamin E	0.5 mcg
Calcium	63 mg
Iron	3.7 mg
Magnesium	69 mg
Potassium	525 mg
Zinc	2 mg

Chickpeas appear to be very good at improving the balance and type of fats in our blood. In recent trials, regular consumption gave the testers lower total and LDL cholesterol and reduced triglyceride levels compared with people who ate other types of high-fibre food. Chickpeas also have a positive effect on insulin and blood sugar levels so are a recommended food for diabetics. Their high fibre content supports the digestive system and can help prevent diverticulitis and colon cancer, while the plant chemicals chickpeas contain – isoflavones, saponins and phytosterols – protect against both heart disease and cancers. They also contain other heart-friendly nutrients including magnesium and folate.

• Very high in fibre to support the digestive system.
• Good source of most of the B vitamins including folate.
• Rich in minerals, including iron, zinc, magnesium, potassium and calcium.
• Contains several plant chemicals to fight heart disease and cancer.

Practical tips:
Soak dry chickpeas for 4 hours or more before boiling for 5 minutes then simmering for 1½ hours, or until soft. Canned cooked chickpeas have a similar nutrient profile to those cooked from raw. Try using them in a vegetable Moroccan tagine with butternut squash, green peppers, apricots and harissa.

Spicy falafels

SERVES 4

400 g/14 oz canned chickpeas,
    drained and rinsed
1 small red onion, chopped
2 garlic cloves, crushed
2 tsp ground coriander
1½ tsp ground cumin
1 tsp ground star anise
1 fresh red chilli, chopped
1 egg white
½ tsp gluten-free baking powder
gram flour, for shaping
sunflower oil, for deep-frying
salt and pepper

Salad

1 large orange
2 tbsp extra virgin olive oil
55 g/2 oz rocket leaves
salt and pepper

Method

1 Place the chickpeas, onion, garlic, coriander, cumin, anise, chilli, egg white and salt and pepper in a blender or food processor and process to a firm, but still textured, paste. Stir in the baking powder.

2 Use a little gram flour on your hands to shape the mixture into 12 small balls.

3 To make the salad, cut all the peel and white pith from the orange and lift out the segments, catching the juice. Whisk the orange juice with the olive oil and season to taste. Lightly toss the orange segments and rocket with the dressing.

4 Heat a 2.5-cm/1-inch depth of oil in a large pan to 180°C/350°F, or until a cube of bread browns in 30 seconds. Fry the falafels for about 2 minutes, until golden brown.

5 Drain the falafels on kitchen paper and serve with the salad.

23

SPLIT PEAS

Split peas are a sweet-tasting, quick-cook pulse and make an ideal nutrient-rich addition to a meal to supply carbs in a gluten-free diet.

NUTRIENTS PER AVERAGE PORTION (60 G/2¼ oz DRY WEIGHT) SPLIT PEAS

Calories	205
Protein	14.7 g
Fat	0.7 g
Carbohydrate	36 g
Fibre	15.3 g
Vitamin A	26 mcg
Vitamin B1	0.4 mg
Vitamin B5	1 mg
Vitamin B6	0.3 g
Choline	57 mg
Folate	164 mcg
Niacin	1.7 mg
Calcium	33 mg
Iron	2.6 mg
Magnesium	69 mg
Phosphorous	220 mg
Potassium	589 mg
Zinc	1.8 mg
Beta-carotene	53 mcg

While the amount of some of the minerals is not quite as high as in some other pulses, split peas contain more vitamin A, which is important for good vision and skin, and some beta-carotene, which converts to vitamin A in our bodies. They are also particularly high in niacin and choline (two B vitamins that improve the blood fats profile), potassium (for healthier blood pressure levels) and phosphorous (for strong teeth). Rich in total and soluble fibre, split peas help ease digestive upsets and improve bowel function. They also contain isoflavones which may help reduce the risk of some cancers, and phytosterols which can lower cholesterol.

• Rich in several nutrients and chemicals to improve blood and heart health.
• A useful source of vitamin A.
• Fibre helps ease bowel problems and digestive upsets.
• Plant chemicals help to lower cholesterol and reduce the risk of some cancers.

Practical tips:
Split peas are quick to cook and don't even need to be pre-soaked. Add them to boiling water and simmer for 25 minutes, or until tender, or add them straight into the pan as they are for quick and easy soups and casseroles. Split pea dal is a spicy Indian dish often served with rice, and makes a healthy, cost-effective meal.

Split pea and ham soup

SERVES 6–8  (C) (F) (V) (D) (P) (N)

500 g/1 lb 2 oz split green peas
1 tbsp olive oil
1 large onion, finely chopped
1 large carrot, peeled and finely
   chopped
1 celery stalk, finely chopped
1 litre/1¾ pints gluten-free
   chicken or vegetable stock
1 litre/1¾ pints water
225 g/8 oz lean unsmoked ham,
   finely diced
¼ tsp dried thyme
¼ tsp dried marjoram
1 bay leaf
salt and pepper

Method

1 Rinse the peas under cold running water. Place them in a saucepan and cover generously with water. Bring to the boil and boil for 3 minutes, skimming off any foam that rises to the surface with a slotted spoon. Drain and set aside.

2 Heat the oil in a large saucepan. Add the onion and cook over medium heat for 3–4 minutes, until just softened.

3 Add the carrot and celery and cook for 2 minutes. Add the peas, pour in the stock and water and stir to combine. Bring just to the boil and stir the ham into the soup.

4 Add the thyme, marjoram and bay leaf to the pan. Reduce the heat, cover and cook gently for 1–1½ hours, until everything is very soft. Remove the bay leaf. Taste and adjust the seasoning, if necessary. Ladle into warmed soup bowls and serve.

24 RED LENTILS

High in plant sterols and soluble fibre, red lentils are one of the best pulses for anyone with digestive problems. The high iron and zinc content also makes this pulse a valuable addition to a gluten-free diet.

A good source of beta-sitosterol, a plant compound that lowers LDL cholesterol in the blood and is not easy to find in many natural foods, red lentils are also a very good source of easily-digested starch. They are lower in total fibre than green or brown lentils, but the proportion of cholesterol-lowering soluble fibre is a little higher. The reduced fibre content makes these lentils a good choice for anyone with a particularly sensitive gut, prone to bloating and/or loose bowels. Red lentils are rich in iron which can be in shortfall on a gluten-free diet. Iron is important for healthy blood and to prevent tiredness and anaemia. Their zinc content is impressive – a 60-g/2¼-oz portion provides a quarter of a day's RDA of this important immune-booster.

- High in easily-digested starch and soluble fibre.
- Source of beta-sitosterol which can lower LDL cholesterol.
- Rich in energy-promoting iron.
- Very high in the antioxidant zinc to boost the immune system.

Practical tips:
Puréed red lentils form the basis of the most popular version of the Indian spiced dish, dal. Eaten with rice, this makes a high-quality protein meal. Red lentils are usually cooked within 25 minutes and need no soaking, so they make a very quick and pretty soup (try adding to carrot, potato, onion and coriander) or a hearty pâté.

DID YOU KNOW?

The older the lentils are, the longer they will take to cook down to a rich, yellow purée. Rinse dry lentils in cold water before cooking and pick over to remove any shrivelled lentils or stalks.

NUTRIENTS PER AVERAGE PORTION (60 G/2¼ oz DRY WEIGHT) RED LENTILS

Calories	207
Protein	14.9 g
Fat	1.3 g
Carbohydrate	35.4 g
Fibre	6.5 g
Vitamin B1	0.3 mg
Vitamin B6	0.2 mg
Folate	122 mcg
Niacin	0.9 mg
Calcium	25 mg
Iron	4.5 mg
Magnesium	43 mg
Phosphorous	176 mg
Potassium	347 mg
Selenium	4.9 mcg
Zinc	2.4 mg

Spicy carrot and lentil soup

SERVES 4

2 tbsp olive oil

1 large onion, chopped

1 celery stick, chopped

1 potato, diced

6 carrots, sliced

1 tsp paprika

2 tsp ground cumin

1 tsp ground coriander

½ tsp chilli powder, plus extra to
    taste (optional)

175 g/6 oz red split lentils

1.2 litres/2 pints gluten-free
    vegetable stock

2 bay leaves

salt and pepper

fresh coriander leaves,
    to garnish

Method

1 Heat the oil in a large, heavy-based saucepan over a medium-low heat. Add the onion and fry for 7 minutes, stirring occasionally. Add the celery, potato and carrots and cook for a further 5 minutes, stirring occasionally. Stir in the paprika, cumin, ground coriander and chilli powder, if using, and cook for a further minute.

2 Stir in the lentils, stock and bay leaves. Bring to the boil, then reduce the heat and simmer, half-covered, over a low heat, stirring occasionally to prevent the lentils sticking to the bottom of the saucepan. Cook for 25 minutes, or until the lentils are tender.

3 Remove and discard the bay leaves. Transfer to a food processor or blender, or use a hand-held blender, and process the soup until smooth. Return to the saucepan and reheat. Season to taste with salt and pepper and add extra chilli powder, if liked. Ladle into warmed bowls and garnish with coriander before serving.

25

GREEN/BROWN LENTILS

Both high in protein and carbohydrate, green and brown fibre-rich lentils are a tasty way to boost your B vitamin and mineral intake.

Black, brown and deep green lentils tend to have a similar nutrient content and levels. Lentils are a rich source of both insoluble and soluble fibre and isoflavones (all of which help protect against cancer and cardiovascular disease), and lignans, plant compounds with mild oestrogen-like effect which may help keep bones strong as we age. They are rich in B vitamins for nerve health and folate for the reproductive system, and are higher in the antioxidant, anti-cancer mineral selenium than most of the dried pulses. And their very high potassium content can help regulate the heartbeat and reduce high blood pressure.

- Rich in dietary fibre for protection from cardiovascular disease.
- Lignans help keep bones strong and selenium can protect against cancer.
- Great source of several of the B vitamins.
- High in potassium for healthy heart.

Practical tips:
Lentils are one of the few pulses that don't need soaking and are usually tender after only around 30–40 minutes simmering. Cook them in the pot with meat and/or vegetables for an easy stew. They also make excellent burgers or a nutrient-rich soup.

DID YOU KNOW?

Lentils contain naturally occurring chemicals called purines, which can be a cause of gout and kidney stones. Gout sufferers have long been told to avoid lentils but recent research seems to show that plant purines are less likely to cause problems than those that are found in some meats and fish.

NUTRIENTS PER AVERAGE PORTION (60 G/2¼ oz DRY WEIGHT) GREEN OR BROWN LENTILS

Calories	212
Protein	15.5 g
Fat	0.6 g
Carbohydrate	36 g
Fibre	18 g
Vitamin B1	0.5 mg
Vitamin B6	0.3 mg
Folate	287 mcg
Niacin	1.6 mg
Calcium	34 mg
Iron	4.5 mg
Magnesium	73 mg
Potassium	573 mg
Selenium	5 mcg
Zinc	2.9 mg

Tuna, lentil and potato salad

SERVES 4

200 g/7 oz Puy or brown lentils
*2 tbsp olive oil, plus extra for
   brushing*
*300 g/10½ oz baby new
   potatoes, halved*
1 Little Gem lettuce
*4 fresh tuna steaks, about
   100 g/3½ oz each*
*300 g/10½ oz cherry
   tomatoes, halved*
40 g/1½ oz rocket

Dressing
5 tbsp fruity olive oil
1 tbsp balsamic vinegar
2 tsp red wine vinegar
*1 tsp smooth, gluten-free
   Dijon mustard*
1 tsp runny honey

Method

1 Boil the lentils in a saucepan of water for around 30 minutes, or until tender. Drain, tip into a salad bowl and stir in the olive oil.

2 Put the potatoes in a saucepan and cover with cold water. Bring to the boil, cover and simmer for 15 minutes, or until tender. Drain well.

3 Meanwhile, break the outer lettuce leaves off the Little Gem and cut the heart into eight pieces. Arrange on four plates.

4 To make the dressing, put all the ingredients in a clean jam jar, screw on the lid and shake well.

5 Preheat a ridged griddle pan over a high heat. Brush the tuna with olive oil. Cook it in the hot pan for 3 minutes for rare or 5 minutes for medium, turning once. Transfer it to a plate and cut each steak into six chunks.

6 Arrange the lentils, tuna, potatoes and tomatoes over the lettuce, sprinkle over the rocket and spoon over the dressing. Serve immediately.

26 SOYA BEANS

Rich in high-quality protein, soya beans also contain good amounts of minerals, B vitamins and a range of plant chemicals to help keep you healthy.

Soya beans are unusual in that they contain all nine of the amino acids – the 'building blocks of protein' – in amounts comparable to that in animal protein. Unlike most pulses, soya beans are moderately high in fat, most of which is unsaturated and 8% of which is the omega-3 fat, ALA, for heart health. They also contain other nutrients (such as potassium, magnesium, zinc and choline) which protect the heart and several plant chemicals (isoflavones, phytosterols, betaines and saponins) that combat heart disease or cancer. Tofu (or bean curd) is a high-protein, low-calorie food processed from soya beans. It has fewer vitamins and minerals than the natural beans but still contains a good amount of calcium.

• Plant source of high-quality 'complete' protein.
• Contains omega-3 fats.
• Rich in several nutrients and fibre for heart health.
• Good content of the anti-cancer mineral, selenium.

Practical tips:
Soya beans need long soaking – at least 8 hours – then boiling in fresh water for 10 minutes and simmering for around 2 hours, or until tender. Drain and use the beans in soups, stir-fries and stews, or add mashed beans to veggie burgers. Tofu can be bland on its own but is delicious when marinated – grill, stir-fry, add to curries or eat as it is. High-protein soya flour can be used in baking.

DID YOU KNOW?

Tofu was first made from soya beans in China around 2,000 years ago. The process has much in common with that of cheese-making.

NUTRIENTS PER AVERAGE PORTION (60 G/2¼ OZ DRY WEIGHT) SOYA BEANS

Calories	268
Protein	22 g
Fat	12 g
Carbohydrate	18 g
Fibre	5.6 g
Vitamin B1	0.5 mg
Vitamin B6	0.5 mg
Choline	69.5 mg
Folate	225 mcg
Niacin	1 mg
Calcium	166 mg
Iron	9.4 mg
Magnesium	168 mg
Potassium	1078 mg
Selenium	10.7 mcg
Zinc	2.9 mg

Miso and tofu salad

SERVES 4

400 g/14 oz firm tofu, drained
   and cut into 1-cm/½-inch
   slices
1 tbsp sesame seeds
85 g/3 oz mangetout, thinly
   sliced
115 g/4 oz ready-to-eat
   beansprouts
150 g/5½ oz asparagus,
   trimmed and cut into long,
   thin slices
1 courgette, cut into matchsticks
1 Little Gem lettuce, leaves
   separated and cut into long
   slices
25 g/1 oz fresh coriander,
   roughly chopped
85 g/3 oz mixed ready-to-eat
   sprouting seeds, such as
   alfalfa and radish sprouts

Dressing
3 tbsp rice wine vinegar
2 tbsp gluten-free soy sauce
3 tbsp sunflower oil
1 tbsp gluten-free sweet
   white miso
2 garlic cloves, finely chopped

Method

1 To make the dressing, put the vinegar and soy sauce in a clean jam jar, then add the oil, miso and garlic. Screw on the lid and shake.
2 Preheat the grill to high and line the grill pan with foil. Put the tofu on the foil in a single layer. Mark criss-cross lines over each slice using a knife, then sprinkle with the sesame seeds. Spoon over half the dressing, then grill for 8–10 minutes, turning once, until browned.
3 Put the mangetout, beansprouts, asparagus, courgette and lettuce on a platter. Pour over the remaining dressing and toss gently together. Sprinkle over the coriander and sprouts, then top with the hot tofu, drizzle with any pan juices and serve immediately.

Nuts and seeds

While nuts and seeds are almost all high in healthy fats, a rich source of calories and a good source of protein, they each offer a very different range of textures, flavours and nutrients. From the special fats and antibiotics in coconuts through to the anti-inflammatory form of vitamin E found in pumpkin seeds and the high levels of omega-3s in walnuts, this food group is invaluable in your diet and can be enjoyed in so many dishes.

(C) High in carbohydrate

(F) Very good source of fibre

(V) Rich in vitamins and minerals

(D) Particularly good for digestive health

(P) High in protein

(N) Nutrient boost for gluten-free diet

27 COCONUT

The creamy-white flesh of the coconut is high in fat, much of which is a type of saturated fat that is antibiotic and very good for you.

Over 80% of the calories in coconut are from fat and, although much of this fat is saturated, there is emerging evidence that they are very healthy fats of which there are few dietary sources. Several studies show they reduce the risk of cardiovascular disease. One of these fats, lauric acid, seems to have the ability to increase the 'good cholesterol' HDL in the blood. Coconut fats also seem to have a strong antibiotic effect and there is anecdotal evidence that coconut oil may even reverse or postpone the effects of Alzheimer's disease. The nut also contains phytosterols, which have a total cholesterol-lowering effect, and coconut flesh is a good source of fibre.

- One of the few sources of dietary medium-chain fats linked to heart protection.
- Can increase HDL cholesterol.
- Strongly antibiotic.
- May improve symptoms of Alzheimer's disease.

Practical tips:
Coconut flour and dessicated coconut are dried forms of coconut. Use the flour in baking but follow coconut-specified recipes to ensure good results. You can drink coconut water (the clear liquid inside a whole coconut) as it is, while coconut milk is made by pressing coconut flesh to produce a milky liquid and is used in many Asian dishes.

DID YOU KNOW?

Coconut oil is one of the best and healthiest fats you can use for frying. Solid at room temperature, it is slower to oxidize and alter chemically than other cooking oils, particularly those high in polyunsaturated fats. Oxidized fats are thought to contribute to heart disease.

NUTRIENTS PER 50 G/1¾ oz COCONUT FLESH, FRESH

Calories	177
Protein	1.7 g
Fat	16.7 g
Carbohydrate	7.6 g
Fibre	4.5 g
Iron	1.2 mg
Potassium	178 mg
Selenium	5 mcg

NUTRIENTS PER TABLESPOON COCONUT OIL, COLD-PRESSED

Calories	117
Protein	13.6 g

Coconut and mango quinoa

SERVES 4

*300 ml/10 fl oz canned
    coconut milk*
115 g/4 oz white quinoa, rinsed
*1 large ripe mango,
    about 550 g/1 lb 4 oz*
75 g/2¾ oz caster sugar
juice of 1 large lime
*4-cm/1½-inch piece fresh ginger,
    sliced into chunks*
100 g/3½ oz blueberries
4 tbsp toasted coconut chips
4 lime wedges, to decorate

Method

1 Put the coconut milk and quinoa into a small saucepan over a medium heat and bring to the boil. Reduce the heat, cover and simmer for 15–20 minutes, or until most of the liquid has evaporated. Remove from the heat, but leave the pan covered for a further 10 minutes to allow the grains to swell. Fluff up with a fork, tip into a bowl and leave to cool.

2 Meanwhile, peel the mango, discard the stone and roughly chop the flesh (you will need 350 g/12 oz). Put the mango into a food processor with the sugar and lime juice. Squeeze the ginger in a garlic press and add the juice to the mango mixture. Process for 30 seconds to make a smooth purée.

3 Mix the mango mixture into the cooled quinoa and leave to stand for 30 minutes.

4 Divide the mixture between four bowls and sprinkle with the blueberries and coconut chips. Decorate with lime wedges and serve.

28 ALMONDS

Almonds, like many nuts, are a high-fat food but this is mostly the heart-protective monounsaturated type. Almonds protect your heart in other ways, too.

NUTRIENTS PER 50 G/1¾ OZ FRESH SHELLED ALMONDS

Calories	288
Protein	10.6 g
Fat	24.7 g
Carbohydrate	10.8 g
Fibre	6.1 g
Vitamin B2	0.15 mg
Folate	25 mcg
Niacin	1.7 mg
Vitamin E	13 mg
Calcium	132 mg
Iron	1.9 mg
Magnesium	134 mg
Potassium	353 mg
Zinc	1.5 mg

The fat in almonds is over 60% monounsaturated and strongly linked with protection from heart disease by its ability to improve the blood fats profile by lowering LDL and raising HDL. Almonds are also rich in vitamin E – one 50-g/1¾-oz portion contains more than your RDA – and in flavonoids, both of which offer further protection for the cardiovascular system. Vitamin E's other benefits include protection from cancer, skin problems and arthritic aches and pains. A very good source of calcium, the same portion size of almonds provides around a fifth of your daily needs. And research shows that a handful of almonds a day can help people with type 2 diabetes to regulate their blood glucose levels.

- An excellent source of healthy monounsaturated fats.
- Very rich in the antioxidant vitamin E.
- A great source of non-dairy calcium.
- Rich in flavonoids which offer protection for the heart.

Practical tips:
Try to find whole almonds with their brown skins still on – the skins contain most of the beneficial flavonoids and vitamin E, and also help the nuts to stay fresh. Almonds can be used in very many sweet and savoury dishes and make an ideal topping for breakfast cereals or a portable snack. The oil can be used in a salad dressing, while almond flour is a very useful high-protein flour for the gluten-free diet – try it in cookies, crumble toppings and cakes. Store nuts, oil and flour in a cool place to retain the health-giving compounds.

Clementine almond cake

SERVES 8–10

125 g/4½ oz unsalted butter,
   plus extra for greasing
125 g/4½ oz caster sugar
4 eggs, separated
150 g/5½ oz millet flour
2 tsp gluten-free
   baking powder
125 g/4½ oz ground almonds
juice and finely grated rind
   of 2 clementines

Syrup
juice of 4 clementines
100 g/3½ oz caster sugar

Topping
225 g/8 oz low-fat soft curd
   cheese or quark
2 tbsp sugar
2 tbsp extra-thick double cream

Method

1 Preheat the oven to 180°C/ 350°F/Gas Mark 4. Grease a 23-cm/9-inch springform cake tin.

2 Beat together the butter and sugar for 3 minutes, until fluffy. Gradually beat in the egg yolks.

3 Combine the flour, baking powder and ground almonds, then beat into the butter, sugar and egg yolk mixture. Mix in the clementine juice, reserving the rind.

4 Whisk the egg whites until they hold stiff peaks. Fold carefully into the mixture using a large metal spoon. Spoon the batter into the prepared tin.

5 Bake in the preheated oven for 30–40 minutes, until a skewer inserted into the centre comes out clean.

6 Meanwhile, to make the syrup, put the clementine juice and sugar into a small saucepan, bring to the boil. Boil for 3 minutes, until syrupy.

7 With the cake still in its tin, make holes all over the surface with a skewer. Pour over the hot syrup. When it has trickled into the holes, remove the cake from the tin and transfer to a wire rack to cool completely.

8 To make the topping, beat together the curd cheese, sugar and cream. Spread over the cake and sprinkle with the reserved clementine rind.

29

CHESTNUTS

Chestnuts are low in fat and calories, and their high carbohydrate content makes them ideal for use in a gluten-free diet, either as nuts or as a flour.

Compared with other nuts they are unusually rich in starches, which means that their sweet flesh is ideal for making a versatile gluten-free flour. These nuts contain most of the minerals we require, albeit in small amounts, apart from iron and potassium which are present here in useful amounts. Potassium is important to help regulate the fluid in our bodies and to keep blood pressure at a safe level. Chestnuts are also a good source of insoluble fibre, similar to that in grains, which helps to keep the digestive system working well and offers protection against heart disease.

- Lower in calories and fat than most nuts – ideal for those watching their weight and/or fat intake.
- A good source of vitamin C.
- Useful source of potassium for fluid regulation and healthier blood pressure.
- Useful source of insoluble fibre for heart and digestive health.

DID YOU KNOW?

Sweet fresh chestnuts are the only nuts to contain vitamin C in good amounts – a small handful will give you around a quarter of your RDA.

NUTRIENTS PER 50 G/1¾ OZ FRESH SHELLED CHESTNUTS

Calories	98
Protein	0.8 g
Fat	0.6 g
Carbohydrate	22 g
Fibre	2 g
Folate	29 mcg
Vitamin C	20 mg
Iron	0.5 mg
Potassium	242 mg

Practical tips:
Fresh chestnuts can be eaten raw, though they are most often cooked before eating. Roast (after cutting a cross in the top so that they don't explode in the oven) until tender or part-roast to make them easy to peel, then simmer in water or milk. Their starchiness makes them a good stuffing alternative to rice or breadcrumbs. Use chestnut flour in place of cornflour or wheat flour as a thickener for sauces and stews, etc., or mix with other gluten-free flours to make an ideal flour for sweet bakes, such as crêpes and shortbreads.

Pumpkin and chestnut risotto

SERVES 4

1 tbsp olive oil
40 g/1½ oz butter
1 small onion, finely chopped
225 g/8 oz pumpkin, diced
*225 g/8 oz chestnuts, cooked
    and shelled*
280 g/10 oz risotto rice
*150 ml/5 fl oz gluten-free dry
    white wine*
*1 tsp crumbled saffron threads
    (optional), dissolved in 4 tbsp
    of the stock*
*1 litre/1¾ pints simmering
    gluten-free vegetable stock*
*85 g/3 oz Parmesan cheese,
    freshly grated, plus extra for
    serving*
salt and pepper

Method

1 Heat the oil with 25 g/1 oz of the butter in a deep saucepan over a medium heat until the butter has melted. Stir in the onion and pumpkin and cook, stirring occasionally, for 5 minutes, or until the onion is soft and starting to turn golden and the pumpkin begins to colour.

2 Roughly chop the chestnuts and add to the mixture. Stir thoroughly to coat.

3 Reduce the heat, add the rice and mix to coat in oil and butter. Cook, stirring constantly, for 2–3 minutes, or until the grains are translucent. Add the wine and cook, stirring constantly, for 1 minute, until it has reduced.

4 Add the saffron liquid to the rice, if using, and cook, stirring constantly, until the liquid has been absorbed.

5 Gradually add the simmering stock, a ladleful at a time, stirring constantly. Add more liquid as the rice absorbs each addition. Increase the heat to medium so that the liquid bubbles.

6 Cook for 20 minutes, or until all the liquid has been absorbed and the rice is creamy. Season to taste with salt and pepper.

7 Remove the risotto from the heat and add the remaining butter. Mix well, then stir in the Parmesan until it melts. Adjust the seasoning if necessary.

8 Spoon the risotto onto four warmed plates, sprinkle with grated Parmesan and serve immediately.

30 BRAZIL NUTS

Rich in minerals, antioxidants and healthy fats, Brazil nuts can boost your immune system and help protect against cancer.

Brazils contain a unique mix of fats – around 40% of their fat is monounsaturates, which help to boost HDL cholesterol, and around 35% polyunsaturates, which lowers LDL cholesterol. These super nuts are the highest of all foods in the antioxidant mineral selenium, which appears to protect us against cancers and other diseases of ageing. Selenium levels in our staple foods have been dropping in recent decades as farming methods alter, so this nut is an easy way to boost your intake, especially in a gluten-free diet. Don't eat a lot in one go though – see 'Did you know?', left. The nuts also have very good levels of magnesium, calcium and phosphorous for healthy bones and a 20-g/¾-oz portion provides a third of your RDA for vitamin E.

- High in unsaturated fats to improve blood lipids profile.
- Extremely rich in antioxidant, anti-cancer selenium.
- High in vitamin E which boosts your immune system and helps protect skin.
- Rich in a range of important minerals.

Practical tips:
Because of their high polyunsaturated fat content, Brazils should be kept in cool, dark conditions and eaten within weeks to help prevent their fats from oxidizing (going rancid). Eat raw to get more benefit from the healthy fats and vitamin E.

DID YOU KNOW?

While Brazil nuts are a healthy food don't eat them all day long! At around 95 mcg selenium per nut, overeating them could give you selenium toxicity. Four nuts (20 g/¾ oz) will give you just under 400 mcg, which is the recommended upper daily limit.

NUTRIENTS PER 20 G/¾ OZ FRESH SHELLED BRAZILS

Calories	131
Protein	2.8 g
Fat	13.3 g
Carbohydrate	2.4 g
Fibre	1.5 g
Vitamin E	2.9 mg
Calcium	32 mg
Iron	0.5 mg
Magnesium	75 mg
Phosphorous	145 mg
Potassium	132 mg
Selenium	383 mcg
Zinc	0.8 mg

Honey and spice snacking nuts

SERVES 6

75 g/2¾ oz Brazil nuts
50 g/1¾ oz pecan nuts
50 g/1¾ oz cashew nuts
25 g/1 oz pumpkin seeds
1 tbsp sunflower oil
1½ tbsp runny honey
½ tsp ground cinnamon
½ tsp mixed spice
½ tsp black pepper
½ tsp sweet paprika
¼ tsp salt

Method

1 Line a baking tray with baking parchment. Preheat the oven to 140°C/275°F/Gas Mark 1.

2 Combine all the ingredients in a bowl, except for half a tablespoon of the honey, and then spread out onto the prepared baking tray.

3 Place onto the middle shelf of the oven and cook for 10 minutes. Remove from the oven and drizzle the remaining honey over the nuts. Leave to cool, then serve. Store in an airtight container for up to a week.

31

HAZELNUTS

Hazelnuts are a great food to eat for your cardiovascular health as they contain several heart health-boosting nutrients.

Hazelnuts are high in the flavonoid group of plant chemicals, including quercetin and kaempferol, to support heart health. The nuts are also a source of several other beneficial plant compounds including betaine, which helps clear the blood of harmful homocysteine, and phytosterols, which also help improve the blood fats profile by lowering cholesterol. The fats in hazelnuts have further cholesterol-lowering effects – they are mostly monounsaturated and can reduce LDL cholesterol and raise 'good' HDL cholesterol. Hazelnuts are also extremely high in vitamin E and magnesium, two antioxidants which maintain heart health, and in potassium for help in regulating blood pressure.

- High in flavonoids to promote heart health.
- Rich in plant compounds which also support the cardiovascular system.
- Great source of vitamin E, magnesium and potassium.
- Rich in monounsaturated fats to raise HDL cholesterol.

Practical tips:
Buy whole nuts rather than chopped – the chopping process destroys much of the nutrient content and shortens their shelf life. Use as a snack, breakfast or dessert or add to salads and stir-fries. Hazelnut oil – at 120 calories per tablespoon – is even higher in monounsaturated fat than olive oil and makes an ideal salad dressing. Hazelnut flour or meal can be used in a wide variety of baking recipes (store it in the refrigerator or freezer).

DID YOU KNOW?

Hazelnuts are one of the few nuts native to the UK and still grow wild across the country, ripening in October. Other names for hazelnuts are filberts and cobnuts.

NUTRIENTS PER 50 G/1¾ oz FRESH SHELLED HAZELNUTS

Calories	314
Protein	7.5 g
Fat	30.4 g
Carbohydrate	8.4 g
Fibre	4.8 g
Vitamin B1	0.3 mg
Vitamin B5	0.5 mg
Vitamin B6	0.3 mg
Folate	57 mcg
Niacin	0.9 mg
Vitamin E	7.5 mg
Calcium	57 mg
Iron	2.4 mg
Magnesium	82 mg
Potassium	340 mg
Zinc	1.2 mg

Green tea and hazelnut ice cream

SERVES 6

400 ml/14 fl oz canned
    coconut milk
200 g/7 oz creamed coconut
200 g/7 oz caster sugar
3 tsp green tea powder
50 g/1¾ oz roast hazelnuts,
    chopped

Method

1 Place the coconut milk and creamed coconut in a medium
   saucepan over a medium heat. Stir continuously, until both
   ingredients have blended together.
2 Whisk in the sugar and green tea powder. Stir in the chopped
   hazelnuts and set aside to cool to room temperature.
3 Transfer to an ice-cream maker and churn according to the
   manufacturer's instructions. Alternatively, pour the cooled mixture
   into a shallow freezerproof container and place in the freezer. Leave
   to freeze until not quite set, then remove from the freezer, stir and
   freeze again until firm. Store in the freezer until required.

32

WALNUTS

A stand-out healthy food, walnuts are the only nut high in omega-3 fat and are also rich in a special form of vitamin E.

Walnuts are one of the few plant foods to contain a high level of the heart-protective, omega-3 fat alpha-linolenic acid – one of the fats essential in our diet. Unless we eat plenty of fish it is easy to have a shortage of this important fat in your diet, so including walnuts in your diet will help boost your intake. These nuts are also high in gamma-tocopherol, a form of vitamin E that is the focus of much research because of its strong anti-inflammatory effects and its ability to significantly lower LDL cholesterol and reduce the risk of coronary heart disease and prostate cancer. Walnuts can also help with weight and diabetes control.

- One of the few plant foods rich in omega-3 fats.
- Unusual in its high content of anti-inflammatory vitamin E gamma-tocopherol.
- Can help with both slimming and diabetes control.
- A good source of polyphenols, to protect the heart, B vitamins and most minerals.

DID YOU KNOW?

Walnut oil not only tastes great but is one of our richest sources of the essential fat alpha-linolenic acid. Just one tablespoon gives 1.7 g – nearly a whole day's recommended amount.

NUTRIENTS PER 50 G/1¾ oz FRESH SHELLED WALNUTS

Calories	327
Protein	7.6 g
Fat	32.6 g
Carbohydrate	6.9 g
Fibre	3.4 g
Vitamin B5	0.3 mg
Vitamin B6	0.3 mg
Folate	49 mcg
Niacin	0.6 mg
Vitamin E (gamma)	10.4 mg
Calcium	49 mg
Iron	1.5 mg
Magnesium	79 mg
Potassium	221 mg
Zinc	1.5 mg

Practical tips:

Walnuts may go rancid in storage as they are rich in polyunsaturated fats, so buy whole kernels, store in the refrigerator and chop as needed. Eat raw with skins on to get the most benefit from their oils, polyphenols and vitamin E. Try them as a pesto with walnut oil and basil, or sprinkle over breakfast cereal or into a salad with blue cheese and pears, using a walnut oil dressing.

Courgette and walnut bread

MAKES 2 LOAVES

butter, for greasing
385 g/13½ oz gluten-free plain
* flour*
1 tsp gluten-free baking powder
2 tsp xanthan gum
1 tsp gluten-free bicarbonate
* of soda*
1 tsp ground mixed spice
2 tsp ground cinnamon
225 g/8 oz caster sugar
3 eggs
240 ml/8½ fl oz vegetable oil
2 tsp vanilla extract
115 g/4 oz walnuts,
* roughly chopped*
220 g/7¾ oz courgettes,
* finely grated*

Method

1 Preheat the oven to 160°C/325°F/Gas Mark 3. Grease two 450-g/1-lb loaf tins and line with baking paper.
2 Sift the flour, baking powder, xanthan gum, bicarbonate of soda and spices together into a large bowl.
3 In a separate bowl, whisk the sugar, eggs, vegetable oil and vanilla extract to a creamy consistency. Add the flour mixture, walnuts and courgettes to the bowl and fold in to make a smooth batter.
4 Divide the mixture between the two tins and bake in the preheated oven for 55–60 minutes, until firm to the touch.
5 Leave to cool in the tins for 20 minutes before transferring to a wire rack to cool. Let the bread rest on the rack for at least 30 minutes before serving.

33

PISTACHIO NUTS

Pistachios contain several compounds and nutrients that help control diabetes, boost immunity, and reduce the risk of heart disease and eye problems.

They are a particularly good source of fibre and protein, which gives them a low GI, and including them in your diet will help control diabetes. The nuts are also rich in a variety of compounds to help lower cholesterol and help prevent cardiovascular disease. These include beta-sitosterols and resveratrol, both of which may also protect against cancer. Pistachios are a great source of vitamins A and E, for healthy skin, and vitamin B6, which helps in the production of haemoglobin to supply oxygen throughout our bodies and boost immunity. Their high content of the carotenes lutein and zeaxanthin means they are helpful in protecting our eyes from macular degeneration.

- Can help prevent or control type 2 diabetes.
- Contain cholesterol-lowering compounds beta-sitosterols and resveratrol.
- Contain plant compounds that also help prevent cancers.
- Immune-boosting and useful to help protect eyes.

Practical tips:
Pistachios are widely used in savoury and sweet Italian, Middle Eastern and Indian cuisine – from pilafs and pâtés to ice creams and biscuits. They go well with pomegranate seeds and quinoa in a winter salad, add nutrients and colour to a crumb stuffing, and are great in a nut roast. A handful makes a healthy snack.

DID YOU KNOW?

Pistachios – originally from Turkey and the Middle East – get their green colour from chlorophyll, the same chemical found in leaves. It's this that makes pistachios such a good source of carotenes.

NUTRIENTS PER 50 G/1¾ oz FRESH SHELLED PISTACHIOS

Calories	281
Protein	10 g
Fat	22.7 g
Carbohydrate	13.8 g
Fibre	5.2 g
Vitamin A	62 mcg
Vitamin B1	0.4 mg
Vitamin B6	0.8 mg
Vitamin E	1 mg
Calcium	53 mg
Iron	2 mg
Magnesium	61 mg
Phosphorous	245 mg
Potassium	513 mg
Zinc	1.1 mg
Lutein/zeaxanthin	703 mcg
Beta-carotene	125 mcg

Pistachio macaroons

MAKES 24

*55 g/2 oz skinned pistachio nuts,
    plus extra to decorate*
40 g/1½ oz icing sugar
1 tbsp rice flour
2 egg whites
55 g/2 oz caster sugar
55 g/2 oz desiccated coconut
1 tbsp chopped fresh mint

Method

1 Preheat the oven to 180°C/350°F/Gas Mark 4. Line two baking trays with baking paper.
2 Place the pistachio nuts, icing sugar and rice flour in a food processor and process until finely ground.
3 Whisk the egg whites in a clean, dry bowl until stiff, then gradually whisk in the caster sugar. Fold in the pistachio mixture, coconut and mint.
4 Place spoonfuls of the mixture onto the prepared baking trays and press a pistachio on top of each to decorate.
5 Bake in the preheated oven for about 20 minutes, until firm and just beginning to brown. Cool on the baking tray and serve.

34 PEANUTS

Peanuts contain more plant sterols (good for lowering cholesterol) than other nuts and are rich in mood-boosting and heart-protective nutrients.

Peanuts are rich in phytosterols, which can lower cholesterol by up to 15%, and high in antioxidant polyphenols. These include resveratrol to protect the heart, coumaric acid which may protect against stomach cancer and isoflavones that protect against breast and prostate cancers. They are a very good source of vitamin E, an antioxidant linked with heart and arterial health, and are extremely rich in niacin, the B vitamin that improves blood flow to the brain and helps release energy from food. They are also a great source of the mood-boosting amino acid, tryptophan.

- High in plant sterols which can have a dramatic cholesterol-lowering effect.
- Rich in antioxidant compounds to protect the heart and fight cancers.
- High in vitamin E for arterial and skin health.
- Rich source of niacin and monounsaturated fats.

Practical tips:
Buy peanuts in their shells or at least in their skins – they will keep longer and retain more nutrients. They make a great snack sprinkled with a little smoked paprika and roasted, or try them in a carrot and cabbage coleslaw dressed with peanut oil. Roasting the nuts can increase antioxidant levels. Commercial peanut butters often contain sugar and salt, so try making your own – blend shelled peanuts in a blender with a little groundnut oil until you have a good spreading consistency.

DID YOU KNOW?

Peanut (groundnut) oil is almost as high in healthy monounsaturates as olive and rapeseed oils and also contains a small amount of the essential omega-3 fat, alpha-linolenic acid. Peanut oil also has a high smoke point so is ideal for sautéing.

NUTRIENTS PER 50 G/1¾ oz FRESH SHELLED PEANUTS

Calories	284
Protein	12.9 g
Fat	24.6 g
Carbohydrate	8 g
Fibre	4.3 g
Folate	120 mcg
Niacin	6 mg
Vitamin E	4.1 mg
Calcium	46 mg
Iron	2.3 mg
Magnesium	84 mg
Potassium	353 mg
Zinc	1.6 mg

Chicken and spicy peanut salad

SERVES 4

4 tbsp crunchy peanut butter

2 tbsp lemon juice

1 garlic clove, finely chopped

1 tbsp finely chopped fresh ginger

2 tsp sesame oil

1 tbsp soft light brown sugar

1 tbsp gluten-free tamari (Japanese soy sauce)

1 tbsp water

¼ –½ tsp cayenne pepper

2 tbsp finely chopped fresh coriander

2 spring onions, thinly sliced

400 g/14 oz chopped cos lettuce

300 g/10½ oz cucumber, sliced

1 small red, yellow or orange pepper, deseeded and diced

350 g/12 oz cooked skinless chicken breast, diced

Method

1 In a small bowl, combine the peanut butter, lemon juice, garlic, ginger, sesame oil, brown sugar, tamari, water and cayenne. Stir in the coriander and spring onions.

2 In a large serving bowl, toss the lettuce, cucumber and pepper with a few spoonfuls of the peanut dressing. Divide the salad between four serving plates or bowls. Top with the chicken, then drizzle with more of the dressing. Serve immediately.

35

CASHEWS

Cashew nuts contain a good balance of protein, carbohydrates and minerals, and are rich in a type of oil that helps protect the heart.

Lower in fat than many other nuts, cashews contain a good balance of nutrients and make the ideal low-GI food to eat as a snack to maintain steady blood sugar levels while boosting your carb intake. The fat in cashews is mostly oleic acid – a monounsaturated fat which is linked with good cardiovascular health. Cashews are high in magnesium, a mineral that works with calcium to promote healthy bones and teeth and can help to lower high blood pressure. They are higher in selenium, a mineral that may reduce the risk of cancer, than most other nuts and also contain very useful amounts of immune-boosting zinc and fluid-regulating potassium.

- A good source of carbohydrates and protein.
- Rich in oleic acid, linked with heart and arterial protection.
- High in magnesium for healthy bones and teeth.
- Good source of selenium to lower the risk of cancer.

Practical tips:
Unsalted cashews make a great addition to all kinds of recipes. Add a handful of lightly toasted cashews to a vegetarian stir-fry or curry just before you serve to increase the protein content. Add them to hot or cold rice dishes to add crunch and nutrients. Pack some with sunflower seeds and sultanas for a snack ideal for travelling. Store cashews in the refrigerator to maintain the nutrient content, or you can even freeze them for up to a year.

DID YOU KNOW?

Cashews are sold pre-shelled because the shells contain urushiol, a skin irritant (the nuts themselves don't).

NUTRIENTS PER 50 G/1¾ oz FRESH SHELLED CASHEW NUTS

Calories	277
Protein	9 g
Fat	22 g
Carbohydrate	15 g
Fibre	1.6 g
Vitamin B1	0.2 mg
Vitamin B6	0.2 mg
Niacin	0.5 mg
Iron	3.3 mg
Magnesium	146 mg
Phosphorous	297 mg
Potassium	330 mg
Selenium	10 mcg
Zinc	2.9 mg

Cashew and chickpea curry

SERVES 4

150 g/5½ oz potatoes, chopped into bite-sized pieces

3 tbsp vegetable oil

1 onion, chopped

2 garlic cloves, chopped

3-cm/1¼-inch piece fresh ginger, peeled and finely chopped

1 tsp cumin seeds

1 tsp chilli powder

½ tsp ground turmeric

½ tsp ground cinnamon

400 g/14 oz canned chickpeas, drained and rinsed

150 g/5½ oz cashew nuts

350 ml/12 fl oz gluten-free vegetable stock

100 g/3½ oz creamed coconut

chopped fresh coriander, to garnish

cooked rice, to serve

Method

1 Place the potatoes in a large saucepan of boiling water and cook for 10–15 minutes, until tender but still firm.

2 Heat the oil in a large saucepan over a medium heat. Fry the onion, garlic, ginger, cumin seeds, chilli powder, turmeric and cinnamon for 5 minutes, or until the onion is soft and translucent.

3 Stir in the boiled potatoes, chickpeas and cashews, and cook for a further 3 minutes. Stir in the stock and the creamed coconut and stir until the coconut melts into the dish. Reduce the heat to low and continue to cook for 15 minutes, or until thick and creamy.

4 Garnish with coriander and serve immediately with cooked rice.

36 PINE NUTS

Pine nuts are an important source of the omega-3 fat ALA and several other nutrients known for helping to keep your cardiovascular system healthy.

The small seeds are rich in polyunsaturated fat, much of which is in the form of omega-6s, but they also contain a small amount of the omega-3 essential fat, alpha-linolenic acid (ALA). This is one of the two 'essential fats' that must be provided by diet as our bodies cannot make it. ALA can even convert in the body to EPA and DHA, the two unique fats found mainly in oily fish that promote a healthy cardiovascular system and reduce the pain of rheumatoid arthritis. Pine nuts are also high in vitamin E and zinc, two antioxidants to help the heart, boost the immune system and increase fertility. And there are important plant sterols and stanols here – compounds which help lower blood cholesterol and boost the immune system.

- One of few plant foods to contain ALA in significant amounts.
- Helps to promote heart and arterial health.
- Contains immune-boosting antioxidants zinc and vitamin E.
- Helps minimize symptoms of arthritis.

Practical tips:
Pine nuts have a distinctive flavour and delicate texture. Try them in dishes cooked with broccoli, spinach, sultanas and oily fish. They are a traditional ingredient of Italian basil pesto and can be sprinkled over many pasta dishes. Because pine nuts are so rich in polyunsaturates, they go rancid quickly, so store in the refrigerator and use within a month.

DID YOU KNOW?

Pine nuts can come from several species of pine and are harvested from trees in the Mediterranean, Asia and the USA. All have similar nutritional profiles.

NUTRIENTS PER 15 G/½ OZ PINE NUTS

Calories	101
Protein	2 g
Fat	10.2 g
Carbohydrate	2 g
Fibre	0.6 g
Vitamin E	1.4 mg
Iron	0.8 mg
Magnesium	38 mg
Potassium	90 mg
Zinc	1 mg

Sprouting broccoli with pine nuts

SERVES 4

700 g/1 lb 9 oz purple sprouting
   broccoli
3 tbsp extra virgin olive oil
3 shallots, thinly sliced
2 large garlic cloves, thinly sliced
pinch of red chilli flakes
3 tbsp pine nuts, toasted
55 g/2 oz butter
2 tbsp capers, drained
4 tbsp snipped fresh chives
25 g/1 oz Parmesan cheese,
   shaved into wafers
sea salt and pepper

Method

1 Cut off the broccoli florets and slice lengthways if thick. Slice the leaves and stems into 2-cm/¾-inch pieces. Steam for 2 minutes over a saucepan of boiling water, until barely soft. Remove from the heat. Reserve the cooking water.

2 Heat the oil in a large frying pan over a medium-low heat. Add the shallots and fry for 5 minutes.

3 Add the garlic and fry for 2–3 minutes, until just starting to colour.

4 Increase the heat to medium and add the broccoli. Add the chilli flakes and season with salt and pepper. Add 3–4 tablespoons of the broccoli cooking water. Cook, stirring, for 4–6 minutes, until the broccoli is just tender and still bright green.

5 Stir in the pine nuts and check the seasoning. Tip into a serving dish and keep warm.

6 Heat a heavy-based frying pan. When it is very hot, add the butter and sizzle until golden.

7 Remove from the heat and stir in the capers and half the chives.

8 Pour the sauce over the broccoli. Sprinkle with the cheese shavings and the remaining chives.

37

PUMPKIN SEEDS

Pumpkin seeds have an unusual balance of omega fats and high levels of vitamin E – essential for good health and important in minimizing the risk of several diseases.

It is not just the type of fat that we eat (saturated, mono- or polyunsaturated) that is important for disease prevention but the ratio of omega-6s and omega-3s (two types of polyunsaturates). Many people have much more omega-6 than is healthy and too little omega-3. Pumpkin seed oil has an almost perfect ratio of 3:1. The seeds are also one of the few plant foods to contain a significant amount of vitamin E in the form of gamma-tocopherol, which is strongly anti-inflammatory and is linked to a reduction in the risk of some cancers and heart disease. Pumpkin seeds are also high in plant sterols which can lower LDL cholesterol, raise HDL and reduce blood pressure.

- Perfect balance of omega-6 and omega-3 fats to protect from disease.
- High in anti-inflammatory vitamin E gamma-tocopherol for further disease protection.
- Rich in several minerals including zinc and magnesium.
- Contain plant sterols to lower LDL and raise HDL cholesterol.

Practical tips:
Pumpkin seeds are almost always sold with the outer pale shell removed although it is perfectly edible. Add the seeds to shop-bought muesli or eat mixed with chopped fruit and yogurt. Try them lightly roasted in the oven as a snack or sprinkle over salads. Grind or chop them and add to a veggie burger mix. Use pumpkin seed oil in salad dressings or drizzled over a nut roast.

DID YOU KNOW?

Make your own: you can dry the seeds from the centre of any pumpkin or squash and then roast them gently on a low heat for about 20 minutes or so.

NUTRIENTS PER 30 G/1 oz PUMPKIN SEEDS

Calories	168
Protein	9 g
Fat	14.7 g
Carbohydrate	3.2 g
Fibre	1.8 g
Niacin	1.5 mg
Vitamin E (gamma)	10.5 mg
Iron	2.6 mg
Magnesium	178 mg
Phosphorous	170 mg
Potassium	243 mg
Zinc	2.3 mg

Indian spiced slaw

SERVES 4 (F)(V)(D)(N)

175 g/6 oz red cabbage,
    shredded
40 g/1½ oz kale, shredded
1 red apple, cored and
    coarsely grated
1 large carrot, coarsely
    grated

Topping
2 tbsp pumpkin seeds
2 tbsp sunflower seeds
2 tbsp flaked almonds
½ tsp gluten-free garam
    masala
¼ tsp ground turmeric
1 tbsp sunflower oil

Dressing
150 g/5½ oz natural yogurt
1 tsp gluten-free garam
    masala
¼ tsp ground turmeric
salt and pepper

Method

1 To make the topping, preheat a frying pan over a medium heat. Put the pumpkin seeds, sunflower seeds, almonds, garam masala and turmeric in the hot pan and pour on the oil. Cook for 3–4 minutes, stirring often, until the almonds are golden-brown. Leave to cool.

2 To make the dressing, put the yogurt, garam masala and turmeric in a large bowl, then season to taste with salt and pepper and stir well.

3 Add the cabbage, kale, apple and carrot to the bowl and toss gently together. Divide the salad between four bowls, sprinkle on the topping and serve.

38

SESAME SEEDS

Even in small amounts, tiny sesame seeds can offer a boost to your nutrient intake. They are rich in important fibres, minerals and plant sterols.

The fibre content of sesame seeds is unusual as it is high in sesamin and sesamolin, two members of the lignan group of fibres that both lower LDL and blood pressure and can enhance the effect of vitamin E in the diet. The rich sterol content of the seeds also enhances the cholesterol-lowering effect. The seeds contain a good range of minerals and are very high in bone-boosting calcium. They also have a very high copper content – an anti-inflammatory mineral linked with protection from the symptoms of arthritis. Tahini is a ground sesame seed paste very rich in all the nutrients contained in the seeds and sesame seed oil contains a good balance of monounsaturated and polyunsaturated fats.

• Contains special types of fibre that boost cardiovascular health.
• Very rich in antioxidant vitamin E.
• High in copper which can help reduce arthritic symptoms.
• Very good source of calcium.

Practical tips:
Sprinkle the seeds on vegetables, such as broccoli or spinach, before serving or add to grain salads. Grind the seeds beforehand to help the body absorb the nutrients more easily. Tahini is an essential ingredient of the popular Middle Eastern purées, baba ganoush and hummus. Try mixing extra tahini into shop-bought hummus to enhance the flavour of the dip. Use sesame oil for stir-frying or, to get the most from its distinctive flavour, sprinkle a little on food before serving.

DID YOU KNOW?

Cold-pressed sesame oil makes an excellent healthy choice for salads as it contains more vitamin E and nutrients than oils from other extraction methods. It is also less likely to oxidize when fried at high temperatures, so is ideal for stir-fries.

NUTRIENTS PER 15 G/½ OZ SESAME SEEDS

Calories	86
Protein	2.6 g
Fat	7.5 g
Carbohydrate	3.5 g
Fibre	1.8 g
Calcium	146 mg
Iron	2.2 mg
Magnesium	53 mg
Potassium	70 mg
Zinc	1.2 mg

Toffee bananas

SERVES 4

70 g/2½ oz gluten-free self-
   raising flour
1 egg, beaten
5 tbsp iced water
4 large, ripe bananas
3 tbsp lemon juice
2 tbsp rice flour
vegetable oil, for deep-frying

Toffee

115 g/4 oz caster sugar
4 tbsp iced water, plus an extra
   bowl of iced water for setting
2 tbsp sesame seeds

Method

1 Sift the flour into a bowl. Make a well in the centre, add the egg and iced water and whisk to a smooth batter.

2 Peel the bananas and cut into 5-cm/2-inch pieces. Gently shape them into balls with your hands. Brush with lemon juice to prevent discolouration, then roll in rice flour to coat. Pour the oil into a saucepan to a depth of 6 cm/2½ inches and preheat to 190°C/375°F, or until a cube of bread browns in 30 seconds. Coat the bananas in the batter and cook in batches in the hot oil for about 2 minutes each, until golden. Lift them out and drain on kitchen paper.

3 To make the toffee, put the sugar into a small saucepan over low heat. Add the water and heat, stirring, until the sugar dissolves. Simmer for 5 minutes, remove from the heat and stir in the sesame seeds. Toss the banana balls in the toffee, scoop them out and drop into the bowl of iced water to set. Lift them out and divide between individual serving bowls. Serve hot.

39

SUNFLOWER SEEDS

Sunflower seeds are packed with important nutrients often lacking in a gluten-free diet, which offer protection against several major diseases.

These seeds are one of the richest in vitamin E. Natural vitamin E (rather than in supplement form) is a valuable antioxidant, protecting us from the diseases of ageing, including cardiovascular disease, cancers and arthritis. A 30-g/1-oz portion of sunflower seeds will give you about two-thirds of your RDA. It also provides a quarter of your selenium RDA to protect against cancer and a quarter of your vitamin B6. This vitamin helps clear the blood of homocysteine, high levels of which contribute to heart disease. The seeds are particularly rich in cholesterol-lowering plant sterols, and sunflower oil is a major source of the essential omega-6 fat, linoleic acid.

- Rich in vitamins B1 and E, and selenium, all of which may be low in the average gluten-free diet.
- Offer protection from cardiovascular disease, arthritis and cancer.
- High in plant sterols to lower cholesterol.
- An excellent source of vitamin B6, niacin, folate, magnesium and zinc.

Practical tips:
Store sunflower seeds in a cool, dry, dark place in an airtight container and eat within 3 months as their very high polyunsaturates content makes them vulnerable to spoiling. Add the seeds to breakfast cereals and salads, or to a nut, seed and dried fruit mix to boost nutrient content. Virgin sunflower oil is delicious in a salad dressing or mixed with olive oil to make a mayonnaise.

DID YOU KNOW?

If you use refined sunflower oil for high-temperature cooking, don't save it and re-use it as frequent re-heating of omega-6 oils produces toxins which may damage your health.

NUTRIENTS PER 30 G/1 oz SUNFLOWER SEEDS

Calories	175
Protein	6.2 g
Fat	15.4 g
Carbohydrate	6 g
Fibre	2.6 g
Vitamin B6	0.4 mg
Folate	68 mcg
Niacin	2.5 mg
Vitamin E	10.5 mg
Calcium	23 mg
Iron	1.6 mg
Magnesium	98 mg
Potassium	194 mg
Selenium	16 mcg
Zinc	1.5 mg

Apple and seed muesli

MAKES 10 SERVINGS

75 g/2¾ oz sunflower seeds
50 g/1¾ oz pumpkin seeds
*90 g/3¼ oz shelled hazelnuts,
  roughly chopped*
125 g/4½ oz buckwheat flakes
125 g/4½ oz rice flakes
125 g/4½ oz millet flakes
*115 g/4 oz no-soak dried apple,
  roughly chopped*
*115 g/4 oz dried stoned dates,
  roughly chopped*

Method

1 Heat a non-stick frying pan over medium heat. Add the seeds and hazelnuts and lightly toast, shaking the pan frequently, for 4 minutes, or until golden-brown. Transfer to a large bowl and leave to cool.

2 Add the flakes, apple and dates to the bowl and mix thoroughly until combined. Store the muesli in an airtight jar or container.

40 FLAXSEEDS

Tiny flaxseeds (linseeds) have an almost unique fat profile with a remarkably high level of beneficial omega-3 fats.

Flaxseeds are the richest of all commonly eaten plant foods in the essential fat alpha-linolenic acid (ALA), one of the omega-3 fats which experts say we should get more of in our diets. Over 50% of the oil in flaxseeds is ALA. The seeds are a very useful food for vegetarians as the ALA converts to the fats EPA and DHA in the body – these are the special very long-chain fats found in oily fish and are both anti-inflammatory and protect against cardiovascular disease. Some research shows that the omega-3 fats can also improve memory and help prevent depression and breast cancer. The seeds contain good amounts of soluble and insoluble fibre so are a good digestive aid. Cold-pressed flaxseed oil contains all the beneficial compounds found in the seeds in an easily digested form.

- Highest of all plant foods in omega-3 fats.
- Anti-inflammatory and protects against cardiovascular disease.
- May help improve memory, ease depression and reduce the risk of breast cancer.
- Fibre content helps digestion.

Practical tips:
Store the seeds in a cool, dark, dry place to keep them fresh and use within a month. The nutrients and oils are harder to digest from whole seeds so it is a good idea to grind them before use. Add ground seeds to your breakfast cereal or yogurt, or sprinkle onto salads and into casseroles and vegetable dishes before serving. And use a little of the oil in salad dressings or sprinkled on steamed vegetables. Do not use the oil for cooking though.

DID YOU KNOW?

You need only 2 tablespoons of flaxseeds or their oil per day to see a reduction in LDL cholesterol, but as it has a low smoke point don't use the oil for cooking.

NUTRIENTS PER 15 G/½ oz FLAXSEEDS

Calories	80
Protein	2.7 g
Fat	6.3 g
Carbohydrate	4.3 g
Fibre	4.1 g
Calcium	38 mg
Iron	0.9 mg
Magnesium	59 mg
Potassium	122 mg
Zinc	0.6 mg

Three-seed salad

SERVES 4 (F) (V) (D) (N)

115 g/4 oz baby spinach
*½ oakleaf lettuce, leaves
    separated and torn into bite-
    sized pieces*
2 celery sticks, sliced
*small handful of celery leaves,
    roughly chopped, plus a few
    extra to garnish*
150 g/5½ oz blueberries
juice of 1 lemon
salt and pepper

Dressing

*2 tbsp sesame seeds, toasted,
    plus a few extra to garnish*
2 tbsp sunflower seeds
2 tbsp flaxseeds (linseeds)
1 garlic clove, sliced
2 tbsp olive oil
juice of 1 lemon
*150 g/5½ oz low-fat natural
    yogurt*
salt and pepper

Method

1 Put the spinach and lettuce in a salad bowl. Sprinkle over the celery, celery leaves and blueberries. Drizzle over the lemon juice, season with a little salt and pepper and toss gently together.

2 To make the dressing, put the sesame seeds, sunflower seeds and flaxseeds in a blender. Add the garlic, olive oil and the lemon juice and season to taste with salt and pepper. Whizz until the seeds are finely ground, then scrape from the sides and add the yogurt. Whizz again briefly until you have a fine paste.

3 Divide the salad between four plates and add a generous spoonful of the dressing to the centre of each plate. Garnish with a few extra sesame seeds and celery leaves and serve.

41

EXTRA VIRGIN OLIVE OIL

Olive oil is the highest of all commonly eaten foods in monounsaturated fats which have several potential health benefits.

Nearly three-quarters of the fat in olive oil is monounsaturated and over recent years several health benefits have been associated with this type of oil. Similarly to polyunsaturates it can help lower LDL cholesterol, but it can also raise HDL cholesterol and offer even more protection against arterial and heart disease. The cold-pressed olive oils contain several plant compounds, including sterols and polyphenols, which increase this heart protective effect, and others which may reduce the risk of cancers and even minimize the symptoms of arthritis and reduce pain. Olive oil also contains a good amount of the antioxidant vitamin E for the immune system, healthy eyes and skin.

- Very high in monounsaturated fat to improve the blood cholesterol profile.
- Cold-pressed oils contain a variety of sterols and plant compounds to protect the heart.
- High in vitamin E.
- Cold-pressed oils can help protect against some cancers and arthritic pain.

Practical tips:
Store olive oil in the dark and use within a few weeks. Try to buy cold-pressed olive oil as it will contain much higher levels of healthy plant compounds. Use olive oil in salad dressings, as a dip, or sprinkled over vegetables as a garnish. Use it instead of other fats for mashed potato and vegetable purées.

DID YOU KNOW?

Light and heat both deprive olive oil of its beneficial compounds. Avoid cooking with cold-pressed and extra virgin olive oil at very high temperatures (over 190°C/375°F) as the beneficial compounds start to degrade around this point and produce harmful free radicals.

NUTRIENTS PER 1 TBSP EXTRA VIRGIN OLIVE OIL

Calories	119
Fat	13.5 g
Vitamin E	1.9 mg

Olive oil-roasted vegetables

SERVES 4

3 red peppers
200 ml/7 fl oz olive oil
250 g/9 oz courgettes,
   thickly sliced
1 fennel bulb, roughly chopped
2 large red onions, roughly sliced
3 white onions, thickly sliced
2 large aubergines, thickly sliced
600 g/1 lb 5 oz ripe tomatoes,
   blanched, peeled, cored and
   deseeded
1 heaped tbsp fresh thyme leaves
1 heaped tbsp fresh rosemary
   leaves
1 tsp sugar
salt and pepper

Method

1 Preheat the grill to high, then place the red peppers on the grill tray and grill until the skins blacken. Turn and grill again, continuing until they are blackened all over. Put them in a bowl and cover with clingfilm to sweat for 10 minutes, then peel off the skin under cold running water. Cut them open and deseed them, then chop the flesh into large chunks.

2 Meanwhile, place a large heavy-based saucepan over a medium heat and add half of the oil. Add the courgettes and fry until they begin to brown. Transfer to a large roasting tin and keep warm. Add the fennel and onions to the pan and fry for 15–20 minutes until they soften, then transfer them to the roasting tin. Add the aubergines and some more oil (they will soak up a lot) to the pan and fry until they begin to brown. Add them to the roasting tin, laid flat in a single layer.

3 Preheat the oven to 190°C/ 375°F/Gas Mark 5. Add the tomatoes, red peppers, thyme and rosemary to the roasting tin. Sprinkle the sugar over and mix through. There should be a tight layer of vegetables, not a stew. If you need more room, use two roasting tins. Season with salt and pepper, drizzle with the remaining olive oil and place, uncovered, in the preheated oven for 40–50 minutes.

4 Eat straight away or leave to cool and eat cold.

42

RAPESEED OIL

Rapeseed oil has a particularly healthy balance of fats for heart health and is probably the best choice of oil for a wide range of culinary uses.

Rapeseed oil is a good source of monounsaturated fats to lower LDL cholesterol and raise HDL, so lowering your risk of heart disease. It is also lower in saturates than olive oil and is the richest – at around 10% of its total fat content – of all the commonly used culinary oils in alpha-linolenic acid (ALA), an omega-3 essential fat that has been linked to heart health and is anti-inflammatory and immune-boosting, and improves insulin sensitivity. The oil has a high burning (smoke) point which means it retains its health benefits and doesn't produce free radicals or carcinogens when used for high-temperature cooking. It is also low in trans fats and high in vitamin E, an antioxidant vitamin linked with healthy skin and protection against cardiovascular disease.

- Low in saturates and with a good balance of mono- and polyunsaturated fats.
- Higher than all other cooking oils in the essential omega-3 fat ALA.
- Good content of vitamin E.
- Extra virgin and cold-pressed types contain good levels of plant sterols.

Practical tips:
Cold-pressed or extra virgin rapeseed oil is a healthy and tasty alternative to other oils in salads and as a dip. They also contain greater amounts of beneficial ALA, vitamin E and compounds than refined rapeseed oil.

DID YOU KNOW?

Rape (a modified version is 'canola' in the USA and Canada) is an annual plant and a member of the brassica family. It has bright yellow flowers in summer and it is the seeds that are so rich in oil. 1½ tablespoons per day will boost your heart health.

NUTRIENTS PER 1 TBSP RAPESEED OIL

Calories	124
Fat	14 g
Vitamin E	2.4 mg

Summer potato salad

SERVES 4

500 g/1 lb 2 oz new potatoes,
  skins on
5 spring onions
1 good handful fresh mint leaves
1 good handful fresh parsley
4 tbsp extra virgin rapeseed oil
1 tbsp white wine vinegar
1 tsp caster sugar
1 tsp gluten-free French mustard
salt and pepper

Method

1 Put the potatoes in a saucepan, cover with water, add a little salt and place over a medium-high heat. Bring to the boil and simmer for about 20 minutes, or until the potatoes are tender.

2 While the potatoes are cooking, slice the spring onions, retaining most of the green parts, and finely chop the mint and parsley. In a bowl, mix together the oil, vinegar, sugar, mustard and seasoning.

3 Drain the potatoes and return them in the pan to the hot hob (switched off) for 1 minute to evaporate any remaining moisture.

4 While the potatoes are still hot, tip them into a bowl and roughly chop them. Add the spring onions, herbs and dressing and stir to mix thoroughly. Cover and leave for 1 hour before serving for the potatoes to absorb the oil and flavourings.

Fruits

Fruits, both fresh and dried, are invaluable because they add so much interest, flavour and colour to any diet. Most are high in vitamin C and potassium, while many are rich in carotenes that your body can convert to vitamin A. This important vitamin can be lacking in a gluten-free diet. Many fruits are also a good source of soluble fibre which helps cardiovascular health, while their varied content of plant chemicals offers protection from many more diseases and health problems.

(C) High in carbohydrate

(F) Very good source of fibre

(V) Rich in vitamins and minerals

(D) Particularly good for digestive health

(P) High in protein

(N) Nutrient boost for gluten-free diet

43 BANANAS

Bananas, with their high starch content and benefits for the digestive system, are a very useful fruit to eat regularly on a gluten-free diet.

While bananas are not as high in vitamin C or antioxidants as some other fruits, they have plenty of other important nutrients. They are the only fruit high in starch rather than sugars; especially true if the banana is eaten before it becomes too ripe. This starch includes a type called 'resistant starch' which ensures the fruit takes longer to be digested. This brings two main benefits – the fruit helps keep bowels regular and is also valuable in managing diabetes as blood sugar levels are less likely to fluctuate. This effect can also keep hunger pangs at bay. Bananas are rich in prebiotics, indigestible carbohydrates that feed probiotics (healthy bacteria) in the digestive system and keep the gut healthy. They are also very rich in potassium for blood pressure and contain the amino acid tryptophan, which helps your body relax.

- Resistant starch content helps bowel regularity; prebiotics keep gut healthy.
- Can help keep blood sugar levels even – a great help in managing diabetes and hunger pangs.
- Very high potassium content helps control high blood pressure.
- Contains tryptophan, which promotes relaxation and sleep.

Practical tips:
While bananas are most often peeled and eaten raw, they can also be cooked. Bake in their skins or grill and serve with maple syrup. Ripe bananas make a delicious ingredient in cakes, muffins and breads – mash and replace some of the sugar with the fruit. Mash ripe bananas and freeze as they are, or use in ice cream or sorbet.

DID YOU KNOW?

Because they have a short shelf life, bananas have been widely eaten across the world only since the twentieth century, after improvements in transport and the advent of refrigeration.

NUTRIENTS PER MEDIUM-SIZED BANANA (100 G/3½ OZ EDIBLE PORTION)

Calories	90
Protein	1 g
Fat	0.3 g
Carbohydrate	23 g
Fibre	2.6 g
Vitamin B6	0.4 mg
Folate	10 mcg
Vitamin C	9 mg
Magnesium	27 mg
Potassium	362 mg

Banana crêpes

SERVES 4

50 g/1¾ oz buckwheat flour
50 g/1¾ oz gluten-free plain flour
pinch of salt
1 large egg, lightly beaten
125 ml/4 fl oz milk
125 ml/4 fl oz water
40 g/1½ oz butter or margarine

Maple syrup bananas

40 g/1½ oz butter or margarine
2 tbsp maple syrup
2 bananas, thickly sliced on the
   diagonal

Method

1 Sift the flours and the salt into a mixing bowl. Make a well in the centre and add the beaten egg, milk and water. Using a balloon whisk, gradually mix the flour into the liquid ingredients. Whisk until you have a smooth batter.

2 Melt 25 g/1 oz of the butter in a small saucepan and stir it into the batter. Pour the batter into a jug, cover and leave to rest for 30 minutes.

3 Melt half the remaining butter in a medium-sized frying pan. When the pan is hot, pour in enough batter to make a thin crêpe, swirling the pan to achieve an even layer.

4 Cook one side until lightly browned, then, using a palette knife, turn over and cook the other side. Slide onto a warm plate and cover with foil while you cook the remaining crêpes, adding more butter when needed.

5 To make the maple syrup bananas, wipe the frying pan, add the butter and heat until melted. Stir in the maple syrup, then add the bananas and cook for 2–3 minutes, or until the bananas have just softened and the sauce has thickened and caramelized. To serve, fold the crêpes in half and half again, then top with the bananas.

44 GRAPEFRUIT

The tart sweetness of fresh grapefruit makes them popular breakfast fruits, but their high soluble fibre content also means they're particularly good for anyone with bowel problems.

Of all fruits, grapefruit is one of the richest in vitamin C – just one fruit contains our whole daily requirement. Vitamin C is a powerful anti-inflammatory antioxidant and can help slow the progress of arthritis as well as helping to prevent cardiovascular disease. It is also linked with improved mood, memory and concentration. Happily, grapefruit is also rich in bioflavonoids which enhance the effects of the vitamin C. Sweet, pink-fleshed grapefruit is a good source of lycopene, the carotene pigment that helps fight cancer and signs of ageing, as well as three other cancer-fighting compounds: limonoids, glucarates and naringenin. The fruits are high in the soluble fibre pectin and have a low GI, making them ideal for diabetics and weight control.

- High in vitamin C for a variety of health protection benefits.
- May help boost mood and memory.
- Rich in plant compounds that protect against cancers.
- Ideal fruit for slimmers and diabetics.

Practical tips:
Make sure the grapefruit is fully ripe before eating as it will then contain the maximum amount of antioxidants – a ripe grapefruit should feel plump and heavy. The easiest way to eat grapefruit is to halve, cut into the segments and spoon out the flesh, but grapefruit pieces are delicious added to salads and salsas. The white pith is also high in beneficial compounds.

DID YOU KNOW?

Anyone on medication should check with their doctor that it is safe to consume grapefruit – the juice can alter the effect of certain drugs, including some that lower blood pressure and cholesterol.

NUTRIENTS PER HALF MEDIUM-SIZED PINK GRAPEFRUIT

Calories	30
Protein	0.5 g
Fat	Trace
Carbohydrate	7.5 g
Fibre	1.1 g
Folate	9 mcg
Vitamin C	37 mg
Calcium	15 mg
Potassium	127 mg
Beta-carotene	770 mcg

Avocado, pineapple and grapefruit salad

SERVES 4

2 pink grapefruits, peeled
  with a knife and cut into
  segments, membrane
  reserved
½ pineapple, sliced, peeled,
  cored and diced
1 large avocado, halved, pitted,
  peeled and diced
finely grated rind and juice of
  1 lime
2 tbsp finely chopped fresh mint
4 outer iceberg lettuce leaves

Method

1 Halve each grapefruit segment, then put them in a salad bowl.
  Squeeze the juice from the membrane over the segments. Add the
  pineapple and avocado, sprinkle over the lime rind and juice and
  mint, then gently toss together.

2 Arrange a lettuce leaf on each of four small plates. Spoon salad into
  the centre of each lettuce leaf and serve immediately.

45 ORANGES

Oranges are one of the best sources of vitamin C, the vital vitamin that boosts the immune system and protects us from signs of ageing, and are packed with other useful nutrients.

Oranges are one of the least expensive fruit sources of vitamin C and are an important part of the diet during the winter when vitamin C levels can dip. Vitamin C is an antioxidant, helping to protect us from cell damage, ageing and disease, as well as keeping the immune system functioning properly. Oranges are also a good source of folate, a B vitamin that can be lacking in a gluten-free diet, and potassium and are higher than most other fruits in calcium – vital for bone maintenance. They have an excellent pectin content, to help control cholesterol, and also contain rutin (a flavonoid that can help slow down or prevent the growth of tumours) and nobiletin, an anti-inflammatory compound.

- Increased vitamin C intake can lessen the severity and duration of colds.
- Flavonoid content protects against cancer and heart disease.
- Good content of pectin, a soluble fibre to protect the arteries.
- Anti-inflammatory – may help reduce incidence of arthritis.

Practical tips:
Store oranges in the refrigerator to retain the vitamin C content (avoid keeping them in a fruit bowl in a warm, light room). Eat some of the white 'pith' of the orange as well as the orange flesh as pith contains higher amounts of fibre and more plant chemicals and antioxidants. The orange peel is also rich in nutrients, but it should be thoroughly scrubbed clean and dried before use.

DID YOU KNOW?

To get the most juice from your orange, it needs to be warm. Bring to room temperature before using or pop in the microwave for 30 seconds.

NUTRIENTS PER MEDIUM-SIZED ORANGE

Calories	65
Protein	1 g
Fat	Trace
Carbohydrate	16 g
Fibre	3.4 g
Vitamin C	64 mg
Calcium	61 mg
Potassium	238 mg
Lutein/Zeaxanthin	182 mcg

Grilled cinnamon oranges

SERVES 4

4 large oranges
1 tsp ground cinnamon
1 tbsp demerara sugar

Method

1 Preheat the grill to high. Cut the oranges in half and discard any pips. Using a sharp knife carefully cut the flesh away from the skin by cutting around the edge of the fruit. Cut across the segments to loosen the flesh into bite-sized pieces that will spoon out easily.

2 Arrange the orange halves, cut-side up, in a shallow, flameproof dish. Mix the cinnamon with the sugar in a small bowl and sprinkle evenly over the orange halves.

3 Cook under the preheated grill for 3–5 minutes, until the sugar has caramelized and is golden and bubbling. Serve immediately.

46

LEMONS

Indispensible in many recipes, lemons are rich in vitamin C for a wealth of health benefits and are packed with other disease-beating chemicals.

All parts of the lemon contain valuable nutrients and antioxidants. They are a particularly good source of vitamin C, while the plant compound antioxidants include limonene (an oil that may help to prevent breast and other types of cancer and may help to lower LDL blood cholesterol) and rutin, which has been found to strengthen veins and beat fluid retention. Lemons contain unique flavonoids called glucosides and kaempferol which can help prevent many types of cancer from spreading. Lemons stimulate the tastebuds and may be useful in dishes for people with a poor appetite.

- Rutin content may help to strengthen veins and prevent fluid retention.
- Flavonoids and limonenes can help to prevent or minimize breast and other cancers.
- Rich in vitamin C to combat arthritis and heart disease.
- Has disinfecting and insecticide properties.

Practical tips:
You can get more juice from a lemon if you warm it slightly (a few seconds in the microwave or in hot water) before squeezing. Always buy unwaxed organic lemons if you want to use the rind. Use lemon juice instead of vinegar in salad dressings or add a squeeze to mayonnaise. The acid and the antioxidants in lemon juice mean that it can help prevent foods, such as apples and avocados, from browning once peeled or cut. The acid also helps tenderize meat so is great in marinades.

DID YOU KNOW?

The level of antioxidants in lemons increases as the fruit ripens, with the highest levels found when the fruit is just on the point of going over-ripe and spoiling.

NUTRIENTS PER MEDIUM-SIZED LEMON

Calories	17
Protein	0.6 g
Fat	Trace
Carbohydrate	5.4 g
Fibre	1.6 g
Vitamin C	31 mg
Potassium	80 mg

Honey and lemon corn muffins

MAKES 12 MUFFINS

125 g/4½ oz gluten-free
*   plain flour*
120 g/4¼ oz cornmeal
55 g/2 oz caster sugar
2 tsp gluten-free baking powder
¼ tsp xanthan gum
1 egg
juice and rind of ½ lemon
50 ml/1¾ fl oz vegetable oil
225 ml/8 fl oz milk
2 tbsp clear honey
1 tbsp glycerine

Method

1 Preheat the oven to 180°C/350°F/Gas Mark 4. Place 12 large paper cases in a deep muffin tin.
2 Place the flour, cornmeal, sugar, baking powder and xanthan gum into a large bowl and mix together well.
3 In a separate bowl, mix together all the remaining ingredients. Add the liquid mixture to the dry mixture and fold in gently.
4 Spoon the mixture into the muffin cases and bake them in the preheated oven for 18–20 minutes, until well-risen and golden. Remove from the oven and cool on a wire rack.

47 APPLES

Apples are one of the most popular fruits in the world and provide us with a range of nutrients including soluble fibre which may help calm a sensitive gut.

Compared with many other fruits, apples aren't very rich in vitamins, but they do contain a good range of plant chemicals. These include quercetin (a flavonoid with anti-cancer and anti-inflammatory properties that may protect against Alzheimer's disease) and anthocyanins for boosting memory. The peel contains ursolic acid, a compound that appears to help maintain muscle bulk and help prevent weight gain, as well as helping to lower cholesterol. Apples are also a valuable source of pectin, a type of soluble fibre which can help lower LDL cholesterol, protect the heart and circulation and help prevent colon cancer. These low-GI fruits also help keep hunger at bay by releasing the hormone GLP-1 which sends 'I'm full' signals to the brain.

- Rich in plant chemicals for a range of health benefits.
- High soluble fibre content can improve the blood lipids profile and reduce LDL cholesterol.
- A low-GI food, ideal for anyone watching their weight.

Practical tips:
Apple skin contains up to five times more plant chemicals than the flesh, so whenever possible eat the skin (wash first and/or buy organic) and choose red-skinned apples which contain more beneficial compounds. When slicing apples put the slices into a bowl of water with the juice of a lemon to prevent the flesh browning (oxidizing). Eat a raw, whole apple when you can – they retain more nutrients than cooked or juiced apple.

DID YOU KNOW?

Adults who regularly eat apples have smaller waistlines, less abdominal fat and lower blood pressure than those who don't. If making a dish with cooking apples, add cinnamon which reduces the amount of sugar you need to add.

NUTRIENTS PER MEDIUM-SIZED APPLE (115 G/4 OZ)

Calories	60
Protein	Trace
Fat	Trace
Carbohydrate	16 g
Fibre	2.8 g
Vitamin C	5 mg
Potassium	123 mg

Apple and plum crumble

SERVES 4

*4 apples, peeled,
   cored and diced*
*5 plums, halved, stoned and
   quartered*
4 tbsp fresh apple juice
25 g/1 oz soft light brown sugar

Topping
115 g/4 oz gluten-free plain flour
75 g/2¾ oz butter, diced
25 g/1 oz buckwheat flakes
25 g/1 oz rice flakes
25 g/1 oz sunflower seeds
*50 g/1¾ oz soft light brown
   sugar*
¼ tsp ground cinnamon

Method

1 Preheat the oven to 180°C/350°F/Gas Mark 4. Mix the apples, plums, apple juice and sugar together in a 23-cm/9-inch round pie dish.

2 To make the topping, sift the flour into a mixing bowl and rub in the butter with your fingertips until it resembles coarse breadcrumbs. Stir in the buckwheat and rice flakes, sunflower seeds, sugar and cinnamon, then spoon the topping over the fruit in the dish.

3 Bake the crumble in the preheated oven for 30–35 minutes, or until the topping is lightly browned and crisp.

48 PEARS

Pears are a particularly useful winter fruit as they store well and are just as tasty cooked or raw. They are an ideal fruit for anyone with a sensitive digestive system.

Pears contain hydroxycinnamic acids – antioxidants that are anti-cancer and anti-bacterial and may help prevent gastroenteritis. They are also high in soothing, soluble fibre pectin and have the lowest recorded rate of any fruit in provoking allergic reactions. This makes the fruit supremely useful for anyone who has a sensitive digestive system. They are also rich in flavonoids, which are not only anti-inflammatory but can also improve insulin sensitivity and help protect against type 2 diabetes. With a useful vitamin C and potassium content they are an excellent food for all the family and are one of the few fruits recommended for young infants.

- Safe fruit for most children and people who suffer from food allergies and a sensitive gut.
- A good source of a range of nutrients including vitamin C and potassium.
- Contains several plant chemicals including anti-bacterial hydroxycinnamic acids and anti-inflammatory flavonoids.
- Can help protect against type 2 diabetes.

Practical tips:
Much of the fibre in pears is in the skin, so it is best to simply wash the fruit and not peel it unless absolutely necessary. Pears tend to brown easily once cut open – sprinkle the cut sides with lemon juice to prevent this. An ideal snack or lunchbox fruit, pears are also very versatile – they can be baked, sautéed or poached, used in mixed fruit compotes or crumbles, tarts and pies.

DID YOU KNOW?

Pear cultivation began in Western Asia and dates back at least 3,000 years. There is even some evidence of pears being grown as long ago as the early Stone Age.

NUTRIENTS PER MEDIUM-SIZED PEAR (150 G/5½ OZ)

Calories	86
Protein	0.6 g
Fat	Trace
Carbohydrate	23 g
Fibre	4.6 g
Vitamin C	6.2 mg
Potassium	176 mg

Pear, celery, blue cheese and walnut salad

SERVES 4

Ingredients

4 celery sticks
1 large, juicy red-skinned pear
a little lemon juice
3 tbsp chopped fresh
    flat-leaf parsley
150 g/5½ oz dark green salad
    leaves, such as rocket,
    watercress or baby spinach
100 g/3½ oz blue cheese,
    broken into small chunks
4 tbsp roughly chopped walnuts
sea salt flakes

Dressing

1 large, juicy pear
1 tbsp lemon juice
4 tbsp walnut oil
¼ tsp black pepper
sea salt flakes

Method

1 Trim the celery and remove the strings with a swivel peeler. Slice into bite-sized pieces. Put into a shallow bowl.

2 Quarter and core the pear but do not peel. Slice each quarter lengthways into thin segments. Add to the celery. Sprinkle with a little lemon juice to prevent discoloration.

3 To make the dressing, quarter and core the pear. Slice one quarter lengthways into thin segments. Add to the pears in the bowl. Peel and roughly chop the remaining pear quarters.

4 Process the chopped pear with the remaining dressing ingredients with a hand-held blender. Process for 30 seconds until very smooth. Scrape into a small bowl.

5 Toss the celery and pears with about 5 tablespoons of the dressing, or enough to just coat. Stir in the parsley. Season with a little salt.

6 Arrange the salad leaves on individual plates. Pile the pear and celery mixture attractively on top. Sprinkle with the cheese and nuts. Spoon the remaining dressing over the salad and serve.

49 GRAPES

Grapes are rich in polyphenols – compounds that protect our hearts and circulation and help lower cholesterol. They are relatively high in calories so are very useful in a gluten-free diet.

Most of the beneficial compounds are in grape skins. Black, purple and red varieties contain much higher levels of the dark pigments (anthocyanins) and the flavonoid quercetin than green grapes. Both of these may help prevent heart and cardiovascular disease and cancer. Two more compounds in grapes – resveratrol and tannins – have been linked to the prevention or inhibition of cancer and heart disease, degenerative nerve disease, viral infections and Alzheimer's disease. With their relatively high sugar content, grapes are higher in carbohydrate and calories than many other fruits and so can be a useful source of carbs in a gluten-free diet. Raisins and sultanas (dried grapes) are a concentrated form of the fruit with a high carb and good iron content, but little vitamin C.

- Rich source of a variety of plant compounds.
- Help to prevent cancer.
- Encourage a healthy cardiovascular system, improve blood cholesterol and have anti-blood clotting effect.
- Anti-viral and anti-fungal action.

Practical tips:
Wash grapes before use, unless organic, as they may be sprayed with pesticides. Store uncovered in the refrigerator or a cool room to preserve vitamin C. Slice grapes for fruit salad at the last minute, to prevent oxidation (loss of vitamin C and browning). Grapes are delicous raw but can also be used for making juice, jellies, vinegar and sauces to accompany fish and chicken.

DID YOU KNOW?

Grapes can be frozen: wash and dry them individually and place on a tray covered in robust kitchen paper. Freeze on the tray then bag up.

NUTRIENTS PER AVERAGE SERVING (100 g/3½ oz)

Calories	70
Protein	0.7 g
Fat	Trace
Carbohydrate	18 g
Fibre	0.9 g
Vitamin C	10.8 mg
Calcium	14 mg
Potassium	191 mg

Quinoa, grape and almond salad

SERVES 2

135 g/4¾ oz white quinoa,
    rinsed
300 ml/10 fl oz water
½ tsp salt
1½ tsp lemon juice
1½ tsp gluten-free tamari
    (Japanese soy sauce)
1½ tsp toasted sesame oil,
    plus extra for drizzling
85 g/3 oz mangetout
150 g/5½ oz seedless black
    grapes, halved
2 tbsp almonds,
    halved lengthways
3 tbsp snipped fresh chives
2 Little Gem lettuces,
    leaves separated
white pepper

Method

1 Put the quinoa into a saucepan with the water and salt. Bring to the boil, then reduce the heat, cover and simmer for 15 minutes. Remove from the heat, but leave the pan covered for a further 5 minutes to allow the grains to swell. Fluff up with a fork and set aside.

2 Whisk together the lemon juice, tamari, sesame oil and a little white pepper. Pour over the quinoa, and fluff up with a fork. Tip into a shallow dish and leave to cool.

3 Plunge the mangetout into a saucepan of boiling water for 30 seconds, then drain. Leave to dry, then slice each mangetout diagonally in two.

4 Carefully stir the mangetout, grapes, almonds and chives into the quinoa.

5 Arrange the lettuce leaves around the edges of two plates. Pile the quinoa mixture in the centre, drizzle over a little more sesame oil and serve.

50 MELON

Juicy melon flesh is rich in vitamin C and a great source of potassium and carotenes, providing a wealth of health benefits.

We love melon as a refreshing, aromatic fruit – at over 90% water content it helps keep us hydrated and the juice needs no added sugar to make it palatable. Melon flesh varies in colour from creamy through yellow to orange and red, and in general the deeper the colour, the more carotenes (which protect against cancer and help heart health) the fruit contains. So cantaloupe and watermelon are two good varieties to choose. All melons are a great source of vitamin C for a healthy immune system and heart, and potassium, which helps prevent fluid retention and is vital for a healthy blood pressure level. Several varieties are high in bioflavonoids, plant chemicals that have anti-cancer, anti-heart disease and anti-ageing properties.

- An average slice of melon contains half a day's RDA of vitamin C for adults.
- High potassium content helps prevent fluid retention and high blood pressure.
- Soluble fibre content helps lower LDL blood cholesterol.
- Watermelon contains citrulline, an amino acid that improves blood flow to muscles which can help during exercise.

Practical tips:
Try to buy melon still in its skin – if you choose ready-cut melon its vitamin C content will be diminished. Wash and dry melons thoroughly before cutting to reduce the risk of food poisoning from dirty skin, and store all cut melon in the refrigerator. Try melon slices draped with Italian cured ham for a simple starter.

DID YOU KNOW?

In some parts of the world, roasted melon seeds are a popular snack – the seeds are a good source of magnesium, iron, zinc and phosphorous.

NUTRIENTS PER AVERAGE SLICE CANTALOUPE MELON (100 G/3½ OZ EDIBLE PORTION)

Calories	34
Protein	0.8 g
Fat	Trace
Carbohydrate	8 g
Fibre	0.9 g
Vitamin C	37 mg
Potassium	267 mg
Beta-carotene	2020 mcg

Melon, Parma ham and pecorino salad

SERVES 4

400 g/14 oz watermelon flesh,
   thinly sliced
400 g/14 oz honeydew melon
   flesh, thinly sliced
400 g/14 oz cantaloupe melon
   flesh, thinly sliced
140 g/5 oz sliced Parma ham
25 g/1 oz pecorino cheese
   shavings
25 g/1 oz fresh basil

Dressing
4 tbsp light olive oil
4 tbsp aged sherry vinegar
salt and pepper

Method

1 Arrange the watermelon, honeydew melon and cantaloupe melon slices on a large serving platter. Tear any large Parma ham slices in half, then fold them all over and around the melon.

2 To make the dressing, put the olive oil and sherry vinegar in a clean jam jar, season well with salt and pepper, screw on the lid and shake well. Drizzle over the melon and Parma ham.

3 Sprinkle on the pecorino and basil. Serve immediately.

51

FIGS

Both fresh and dried figs are a valuable source of dietary fibre and contain useful amounts of minerals for heart health.

Figs contain good amounts of dietary fibre, much of which is soluble, to help protect against heart disease. They also contain enzymes which have a mildly laxative effect so are helpful to ensure a regular bowel. Figs are a good source of potassium, which regulates blood pressure, and they contain calcium, magnesium and natural sterols, all of which are heart-friendly. Calcium and magnesium also work together to keep bones healthy. Figs provide some iron, a mineral which can easily be in shortfall on a gluten-free diet, and contain antioxidant carotenes for eye health and to help lower the risk of some cancers.

- Contain several nutrients to promote heart health and reduce blood pressure.
- Fibre and enzymes help maintain good bowel movement.
- Minerals for bone health.
- Carotenes for healthy eyes.

Practical tips:
Fresh figs are best eaten raw, poached or lightly grilled. They make a light starter or canapé – try stuffing them with soft mozzarella or ricotta cheese. They're also ideal as a dessert or at breakfast. Try them with Greek yogurt and honey. Dried figs are also good this way or can be poached in water or juice to reconstitute. Dried figs have a similar nutrient profile to fresh, per fig.

DID YOU KNOW?

Blend dried figs with a little water to replace sugar in baking – they add a succulent and moist texture.

NUTRIENTS PER MEDIUM-SIZED FRESH FIG

Calories	40
Protein	0.4 g
Fat	Trace
Carbohydrate	10.4 g
Fibre	1.6 g
Calcium	19 mg
Magnesium	9 mg
Potassium	125 mg
Beta-carotene	51 mcg

Tapioca figs

SERVES 6

200 g/7 oz small pearl tapioca
500 ml/17 fl oz rice milk
70 g/2½ oz golden caster sugar
seeds from 2 cardamom pods,
*   lightly crushed*
1 bay leaf
15 g/½ oz sunflower spread,
*   plus extra for greasing*
½ tsp orange flower water
6 fresh figs
pomegranate syrup, for drizzling

Method

1 Grease an 18-cm/7-inch square cake tin. Place the tapioca and rice milk in a saucepan and bring to the boil. Reduce the heat and stir in the sugar, cardamom, bay leaf and the spread.

2 Cover and cook gently, stirring often, for 20–25 minutes, until the grains are tender.

3 Remove and discard the bay leaf and cardamom pods, stir in the orange flower water then spread into the tin and leave to cool. Chill in the refrigerator until set.

4 To serve, turn out the tapioca and cut into diamond shapes. Quarter the figs and arrange on plates with the tapioca shapes. Drizzle with pomegranate syrup and serve.

52 STRAWBERRIES

Strawberries are the fourth richest fruits in antioxidant compounds and have numerous health benefits. Full of soluble fibre, they're an excellent fruit to include in a gluten-free diet.

Strawberries, native to America and Europe, are extremely rich in the antioxidant vitamin C – an average 100-g/3½-oz portion contains nearly a whole day's recommended daily amount for an adult. This essential vitamin helps boost the immune system, prevents arterial damage, speeds wound healing, aids iron absorption and strengthens blood vessel walls. Strawberries also contain other antioxidants, such as anthocyanins and ellagic acid, which can block cancer cells and help prevent some cancers. And strawberries contain good amounts of dietary fibre, with a high proportion of artery- and gut-friendly soluble fibre, folate and potassium.

- Excellent source of vitamin C.
- Contains ellagic acid, a compound with anti-cancer and antioxidant properties.
- Contains anthocyanins which can help lower LDL blood cholesterol.
- Useful source of fibre, potassium, folate and zeaxanthin.

Practical tips:
Smaller strawberries tend to have higher levels of ellagic acid, which is concentrated in the red outer layer, and more flavour. Choose fruit that look plump and glossy – a dull appearance means they are past their best with less vitamin C. Only slice if necessary at the last minute as cutting destroys the vitamin C.

DID YOU KNOW?

Wild strawberries – the ancestors of today's cultivated strawberries – grow easily in most gardens and are an even richer source of nutrients than their giant modern counterparts.

NUTRIENTS PER AVERAGE SERVING (100 G/3½ OZ)

Calories	32
Protein	0.7 g
Fat	0.3 g
Carbohydrate	7.7 g
Fibre	2 g
Folate	24 mcg
Vitamin C	59 mg
Potassium	153 mg
Zeaxanthin	26 mcg

Strawberry roulade

SERVES 6

sunflower oil, for greasing
3 large eggs
125 g/4½ oz caster sugar, plus
    extra to sprinkle
½ tsp almond extract
55 g/2 oz cornflour
70 g/2½ oz ground almonds

Filling

225 g/8 oz cream cheese
1 tbsp icing sugar, plus extra for
    dusting
200 g/7 oz strawberries, hulled
    and sliced

Method

1 Preheat the oven to
180°C/350°F/Gas Mark 4.
Grease a 20 x 30-cm/8 x 12-
inch Swiss roll tin and line with
baking paper.

2 Place the eggs, sugar and
almond extract in a large bowl
over a pan of hot, not boiling,
water and whisk for about
10 minutes, until thick enough
to hold a trail when the whisk
is lifted. Remove from the heat
and whisk in the cornflour, then
fold in the ground almonds.

3 Spread the mixture into
the prepared tin and bake
in the preheated oven for
12–15 minutes, until just firm
and lightly browned.

4 Place a sheet of baking paper
on the work surface and
sprinkle with caster sugar.
Invert the tin over the paper to
turn out the sponge. Remove
the lining paper and trim the
edges from the sponge. Cover
with a clean tea towel and
leave to cool.

5 To make the filling, beat
together the cream cheese and
icing sugar and spread over
the sponge. Top with sliced
strawberries and carefully roll
up from one short edge.

6 Place on a serving plate with
the join underneath, and dust
with icing sugar to serve.

53 BLUEBERRIES

These popular berries are higher than most other fruits or vegetables in antioxidants and pack a powerful punch with many health benefits.

Because blueberries are so rich in nutrients, a relatively small amount (a 50-g/1¾-oz portion) can offer a good level of protection from various health problems. They contain at least 15 of the most-researched antioxidants. For example, they contain the compound pterostilbene, which is thought to be as effective as commercial drugs in lowering cholesterol, as well as helping to prevent diabetes and some cancers. They're high in anthocyanins which can protect against heart disease and memory loss, and in anti-inflammatory, anti-cancer kaempferol. They are also a good source of vitamin C and dietary fibre, and appear to help protect against urinary tract and digestive infections.

- Antioxidant and plant compound-rich berries.
- Contain cholesterol-lowering compound pterostilbene.
- Can help prevent many of the major diseases including heart disease, diabetes and cancers.
- Help beat urinary tract infections.

Practical tips:
The berries are delicious eaten raw (which helps to preserve their vitamin C content) but can also be lightly cooked in a small amount of water (the resulting juice is tasty and vitamin-rich too). They freeze well and lose almost none of their nutrients. Cook from frozen for best results. Add blueberries to your breakfast cereal or blend with yogurt for a smoothie. They will also boost the nutrient content of muffins, cakes, crumbles, pies and fruit salads.

DID YOU KNOW?

A native of North America, the blueberry is the second most popular fruit in the USA with sales having doubled in recent years.

NUTRIENTS PER AVERAGE SERVING (50 G/1¾ OZ)

Calories	29
Protein	0.4 g
Fat	Trace
Carbohydrate	7.2 g
Fibre	1.2 g
Folate	34 mcg
Vitamin C	5 mg
Vitamin E	0.3 mg
Iron	0.7 mg
Potassium	39 mg
Lutein/Zeaxanthin	40 mcg

Yogurt with blueberries, honey and nuts

SERVES 4

3 tbsp clear honey
85 g/3 oz mixed unsalted nuts
8 tbsp Greek yogurt
200 g/7 oz fresh blueberries

Method

1 Heat the honey in a small saucepan over medium heat. Add the nuts and stir until they are well coated. Remove from the heat and leave to cool slightly.

2 Divide the yogurt among four serving bowls, then spoon over the nut mixture and the blueberries and serve immediately.

54 CRANBERRIES

For several years cranberries have been acknowledged for their role in helping us to good health and not without cause – they really are good for you!

Fresh cranberries are quite sour, so are rarely eaten raw but much of their goodness is preserved even when they are cooked. They are also popular when dried and sweetened. One of their biggest plusses is that they can help to prevent, or shorten the duration of, urinary tract infections such as cystitis, and kidney and bladder stones. This is partly because they contain quinic acid and tannins which have anti-bacterial properties. The high levels of these plant compounds may also help protect against stomach ulcers and heart disease and may have a beneficial effect on your digestive health, which may be helpful for people diagnosed with coeliac disease. They are also a good source of the antioxidants vitamin C, vitamin E and beta-carotene, and of soluble fibre, all of which can protect the heart and may lower the risk of some cancers.

- Help prevent and alleviate urinary tract infections.
- High soluble fibre content may help reduce HDL cholesterol.
- Help prevent digestive disorders and stomach ulcers.
- May protect against heart disease and cancer.

Practical tips:
Cranberries have been popular for decades as the major ingredient in cranberry sauce to go with turkey and game, but they are also excellent in jams and chutneys. Dried cranberries (usually with added sugar) are great in fruit salads, sprinkled on breakfast cereal or added to muffins and other bakes.

DID YOU KNOW?

People taking warfarin should avoid eating cranberries or drinking cranberry juice as the berry interacts with the drug and can be very dangerous.

NUTRIENTS PER 100 G/3½ oz FRESH CRANBERRIES

Calories	46
Protein	0.4 g
Fat	Trace
Carbohydrate	12.2 g
Fibre	4.6 g
Vitamin C	13 mg
Vitamin E	1.2 mg
Carotenes	127 mcg

PER 50 G/1¾ oz DRIED CRANBERRIES

Calories	154
Protein	Trace
Fat	0.7 g
Carbohydrate	41 g
Fibre	2.9 g
Vitamin C	Trace
Vitamin E	0.5 mg
Carotenes	17 mcg

Chocolate, cranberry and nut muffins

MAKES 12

250 g/9 oz quinoa flour
2 tbsp gluten-free
    cocoa powder
2 tsp gluten-free
    baking powder
¾ tsp gluten-free
    bicarbonate of soda
½ tsp salt
125 g/4½ oz unsalted butter,
    at room temperature
125 g/4½ oz caster sugar
2 eggs, lightly beaten
1 tsp vanilla extract
finely grated rind of
    1 large orange
225 ml/8 fl oz milk
125 g/4½ oz dried cranberries
50 g/1¾ oz macadamia nuts,
    roughly chopped

Method

1 Preheat the oven to 200°C/400°F/Gas Mark 6. Place 12 paper muffin cases in a muffin tin.

2 Sift together the flour, cocoa powder, baking powder, bicarbonate of soda and salt into a bowl. Tip any bran remaining in the sieve into the bowl, mixing lightly with your fingers.

3 In a separate large bowl, beat together the butter and sugar for about 4 minutes, or until light and fluffy. Gradually beat in the eggs, vanilla extract and orange rind. Beat in the milk and add the flour mixture, a little at a time, beating well after each addition. Fold in the cranberries and nuts.

4 Divide the mixture equally between the paper cases. Bake in the preheated oven for 15–20 minutes, until well risen and a skewer inserted into the centre comes out clean.

5 Transfer the muffins to a wire rack and leave to cool completely.

55

AVOCADO

The delicious avocado is packed with health-giving nutrients, which can be lacking on a gluten-free diet, and is one of the few fruits with an excellent and healthy fat content.

Avocado flesh is very high in monounsaturated fat (which can help reduce LDL cholesterol and raise HDL cholesterol) and is high in beta-sterols, which also lower LDL. The fat has a high content of oleic acid, a fatty acid, and glutathione, both of which can lower the risk of some cancers. Avocados are also rich in antioxidant, immune system-boosting vitamin E and potassium to help control blood pressure. And they are a good source of the minerals zinc and magnesium, a useful source of iron and an excellent source of vitamin C. Intake of all these important nutrients can be low on a gluten-free diet.

- High monounsaturated fat and sterol content to help lower cholesterol.
- Oleic acid helps lower risk of cancer.
- Great source of minerals and vitamin C.
- High in vitamin E which helps protect the heart and boost the immune system.

Practical tips:
Avocados are best served fully ripe and raw as cooking destroys some of the nutrients. The flesh discolours within minutes once cut, so brush cut surfaces with lemon juice or vinegar. Try with mixed salad leaves and a classic vinaigrette dressing. Use mild, nutty-flavoured avocado oil in dressings or for cooking as it has a very high smoke point.

DID YOU KNOW?

If you want to speed up the ripening of an avocado, put it in a paper bag with a banana or an apple. The paper bag will trap the ethylene gas – a powerful ripening tool – produced by the fruits.

NUTRIENTS PER MEDIUM-SIZED AVOCADO

Calories	227
Protein	2.6 g
Fat	21 g
Carbohydrate	12 g
Fibre	9.2 g
Vitamin B6	0.39 mg
Vitamin C	12 mg
Vitamin E	3 mg
Iron	0.8 mg
Potassium	690 mg
Zinc	0.9 mg

Avocado and sweetcorn salad

SERVES 4

200 g/7 oz frozen sweetcorn
1 large avocado, halved, pitted,
   peeled and cut into cubes
175 g/6 oz cherry tomatoes,
   cut into quarters
½ red onion, finely chopped
1 small green pepper,
   halved, deseeded and cut
   into small chunks
40 g/1½ oz kale, shredded
25 g/1 oz fresh coriander,
   roughly chopped

Dressing

finely grated rind and juice
   of 1 lime
2 tbsp olive oil
salt and pepper

Method

1 Put the sweetcorn in a saucepan of boiling water. Bring back to the boil, then simmer for 3 minutes. Drain into a colander, rinse with cold water, drain again, then transfer to a salad bowl.
2 To make the dressing, put the lime rind and juice and oil in a clean jam jar, season to taste with salt and pepper, screw on the lid and shake well to combine.
3 Add the avocado, tomatoes, onion, green pepper, kale and coriander to the salad bowl. Drizzle over the dressing and toss together. Spoon into four bowls and serve immediately.

56 APRICOTS

Apricots, both fresh and dried – packed with nutrients, rich in carbs and low on the Glycaemic Index – are an excellent addition to a gluten-free diet.

NUTRIENTS PER TWO MEDIUM-SIZED FRESH APRICOTS (100 G/3½ oz)

Calories	31
Protein	0.9 g
Fat	Trace
Carbohydrate	7.2 g
Fibre	1.7 g
Vitamin C	6 mg
Vitamin E	0.6 mg
Iron	0.5 mg
Potassium	270 mg
Beta-carotene	766 mcg

PER 30 G/1 oz SEMI-DRIED APRICOTS (3 WHOLE PIECES)

Calories	47
Protein	1.2 g
Fat	Trace
Carbohydrate	10.8 g
Fibre	1.9 g
Vitamin C	Trace
Vitamin E	1.3 mg
Iron	1 mg
Potassium	414 mg
Beta-carotene	163 mcg

Fresh apricots contain a wide range of nutrients for health protection. Particularly important are vitamins A (in the form of beta-carotene) and E, both of which can be short on a gluten-free regime. Other useful nutrients include vitamin C, folate and potassium. Apricots are also ideal fruits for weight maintenance as they are a good source of fibre, are fat-free and are low-GI. The semi-dried, ready-to-eat fruit is a very good source of potassium, iron and fibre, but the drying process loses vitamin C. Dried apricots are relatively high in calories as their water content is diminished, so are ideal as a snack when you're hungry and their low-GI content will keep you full for a long time.

- Contain a range of carotenes, including cryptoxanthin, which may help to maintain bone health.
- High in total fibre and soluble fibre for heart protection and lowering cholesterol.
- Excellent source of potassium.
- A source of vitamin E for healthy skin and immune-boosting.

Practical tips:
Apricots need to be fully ripe in order to maximize their carotene content. Cooking fresh apricots helps the body absorb the carotene and soluble fibre and they are excellent in fruit crumbles or poached in white wine. Dried apricots are good in couscous and other salads, chopped and added to muesli or a cabbage coleslaw, and stewed to serve with yogurt.

Millet porridge with apricot purée

SERVES 4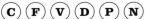

225 g/8 oz millet flakes
900 ml/1½ pints soya milk
pinch of salt
freshly grated nutmeg, to serve

Apricot purée

115 g/4 oz dried apricots,
roughly chopped
300 ml/10 fl oz water

Method

1 To make the apricot purée, put the apricots into a saucepan and cover with the water. Bring to the boil, then reduce the heat and simmer, half covered, for 20 minutes, until the apricots are very tender. Use a hand-held blender, or transfer the apricots and any water left in the saucepan to a food processor or blender, and process until smooth. Set aside.

2 To make the porridge, put the millet flakes into a saucepan and add the milk and salt. Bring to the boil, then reduce the heat and simmer for 5 minutes, stirring frequently, until cooked and creamy.

3 To serve, spoon into four bowls and top with the apricot purée and a little nutmeg.

57

MANGO

Mangoes are a rich source of several important nutrients and are one of the stars of the fruit bowl. They are particularly high in dietary fibre, crucial for a healthy digestive system.

The deep orange flesh of the mango is a clue to one of its major components – the potent antioxidant beta-carotene. This important health compound can protect against some cancers and heart disease. Mango also contains lycopene, a special type of carotene known to protect against prostate cancer, and polyphenols linked with regulation of blood sugar levels. The fruits are also high in vitamin C – one fruit contains a whole day's RDA. Unlike many other fruits, they also contain a significant amount of the antioxidant vitamin E which can boost the body's immune system and maintain healthy skin. Mangoes have a great fibre content too, two-thirds of which is soluble, and good levels of potassium.

- Very high beta-carotene content, associated with cancer and heart protection.
- High levels of pectin – a soluble fibre which helps reduce LDL blood cholesterol.
- Rich in potassium for regulating blood pressure.
- Valuable source of vitamin C and polyphenols.

Practical tips:

Eat mangoes when they are fully ripe and aromatic. They are delicious eaten raw, for maximum vitamin C content, while their carotenes are better absorbed if you eat them with fat. Try Greek yogurt and mango for breakfast or a mango and chicken salad with an olive oil dressing for lunch.

DID YOU KNOW?

Mangoes – first cultivated in India 5,000 years ago – have natural tenderizing properties making them a perfect ingredient for meat marinades.

NUTRIENTS PER AVERAGE-SIZED MANGO (200 G/7 oz)

Calories	120
Protein	1.6 mg
Fat	0.7 g
Carbohydrate	30 g
Fibre	3.2 g
Folate	22 mg
Vitamin C	73 mg
Vitamin E	1.8 mg
Calcium	86 mcg
Potassium	336 mg
Zinc	1280 mcg
Lutein/Zeaxanthin	46 mcg
Beta-carotene	297 mg

Mango sorbet

SERVES 4–6   (C) (N)

2 large ripe mangoes
juice of 1 lemon
pinch of salt
115 g/4 oz caster sugar
3 tbsp water

Method

1 Using a sharp knife, thinly peel the mangoes, holding them over a bowl to catch the juices. Cut the flesh away from the central stone and put in a food processor or blender, reserving some slices for decoration. Add the reserved mango juices, the lemon juice and salt and process to form a smooth purée. Push the mango purée through a nylon sieve into the bowl.

2 Put the sugar and water in a heavy-based saucepan and heat gently, stirring, until the sugar has dissolved. Bring to the boil, without stirring, then remove from the heat and leave to cool slightly.

3 Pour the syrup into the mango purée and mix well. Leave to cool, then chill the mango syrup in the refrigerator for 2 hours, or until completely cold.

4 If using an ice-cream machine, churn the mixture in the machine following the manufacturer's instructions. Alternatively, freeze the mixture in a freezerproof container, uncovered, for 3–4 hours, or until mushy. Tip the mixture into a bowl and stir with a fork or beat in a food processor to break down the ice crystals. Return to the freezer and freeze for a further 3–4 hours, or until firm. Cover the container with a lid for storing.

5 To serve, scoop into individual serving dishes and decorate with the reserved mango slices.

58 NECTARINES

Nectarines are an excellent choice for a summer fruit as they are full of vitamins and minerals. They are also a richer source of potassium than their close relatives, peaches.

The bright red skin and deep orange flesh of a nectarine means it is very high in the compound beta-carotene, the antioxidant that is so important for the immune system. Beta-carotene can also be converted to vitamin A in the body – a vitamin linked with healthy skin, protection from harmful UV rays and growth. Just one nectarine provides around a quarter of your daily vitamin A requirements. The fruit is also very rich in two special carotenes – lutein and zeaxanthin – to support eye health and vision. Nectarines are also a good source of vitamin C, contain a good range of B vitamins and a useful amount of minerals. They are low-GI so their carb content won't cause a spike in your blood sugar levels.

- Rich in vitamin C.
- Excellent source of vitamin A for healthy skin.
- High in carotenes for eye health and vision.
- Low-GI fruit to help prevent blood sugar fluctuations.

Practical tips:
Ripe nectarines bruise easily, so treat them gently. They are delicious on their own, but try them in a sweet/savoury salad with blue cheese and crispy lettuce, or sprinkle them with a little brown sugar and roast. Blitz the flesh in a blender, mix with yogurt and freeze for a healthy iced dessert or snack.

DID YOU KNOW?

Nectarines are a mutant version of a peach with almost identical genes – they aren't related to the plum, as is often thought.

NUTRIENTS PER MEDIUM-SIZED NECTARINE

Calories	62
Protein	1.5 mg
Fat	0.5 g
Carbohydrate	15 g
Fibre	2.4 g
Vitamin B5	0.3 mg
Niacin	1.6 mg
Vitamin C	7.7 mg
Vitamin E	1.0 mg
Potassium	285 mg
Lutein/Zeaxanthin	185 mcg
Beta-carotene	213 mcg

Stuffed nectarines with yogurt

SERVES 4

4 ripe but firm nectarines
140 g/5 oz blueberries
115 g/4 oz raspberries
150 ml/5 fl oz freshly squeezed
   orange juice
1–2 tsp clear honey,
   or to taste
1 tbsp brandy (optional)
4 tbsp Greek yogurt
1 tbsp finely grated
   orange rind

Method

1 Preheat the oven to 180°C/350°F/Gas Mark 4. Cut the nectarines in half, remove the stones then place in a shallow ovenproof dish.

2 Mix the blueberries and raspberries together in a bowl and use to fill the hollows left by the nectarine stones. Spoon any extra berries around the edge.

3 Mix together the orange juice and honey, and brandy if using, in a small bowl and pour over the fruit. Blend the yogurt with the orange rind in another bowl and leave to chill in the refrigerator until required.

4 Bake the berry-filled nectarines in the preheated oven for 10 minutes, or until the fruit is hot. Serve immediately with the orange-flavoured yogurt.

59 PAPAYA

The tropical papaya fruit has a range of vital nutrients which can help keep your digestive system healthy and even prevent some cancers.

The fruit is unique in that it contains papain, an enzyme that helps digest proteins, and chymopapain which is strongly linked with preventing colonic cancer, may help to calm inflammation in the gut and may also help protect against other digestive problems. Papaya is very rich in the carotene lycopene – it is believed that by eating it regularly men can reduce their likelihood of getting prostate cancer. The very high potassium and useful magnesium content means the fruit is ideal for helping to reduce high blood pressure. Half a fruit provides almost a day's recommended vitamin C intake and is also a useful source of calcium for healthy bones.

- Contains the enzyme papain to help the digestive system.
- Very large lycopene content helps to prevent prostate cancer.
- Potassium and magnesium to reduce high blood pressure.
- Good source of vitamin C and calcium.

Practical tips:
A ripe papaya usually has orange and yellow, rather than green, skin. If using papaya in a fruit salad, add it just before serving as the papain can over-soften other fruits in the bowl. The papain also prevents gelatine from setting so papaya shouldn't be used in jellies. Papaya juice is an excellent marinade to tenderize meat or add it to a casserole.

DID YOU KNOW?

The Mayans used to worship papaya trees and called them the 'Tree of Life'. Papayas were said to be one of the favourite fruits of the explorer Christopher Columbus.

NUTRIENTS PER HALF LARGE PAPAYA (100 g/3½ oz EDIBLE PORTION)

Calories	43
Protein	0.5 mg
Fat	0.3 g
Carbohydrate	10.8 g
Fibre	1.7 g
Folate	37 mcg
Vitamin C	61 mg
Potassium	182 mg
Lutein/Zeaxanthin	89 mcg
Beta-carotene	274 mcg
Lycopene	1828 mcg

Chicken, papaya and avocado salad

SERVES 2

2 boneless, skinless chicken
  breasts, weighing about
  150 g/5½ oz each
2 tbsp olive oil
100 g/3½ oz peppery green
  salad leaves, such as rocket,
  mizuna, curly endive and
  watercress
1 large papaya, peeled,
  deseeded and thickly sliced
1 ripe avocado, peeled, stoned
  and thickly sliced
25 g/1 oz toasted hazelnuts,
  halved
2 tbsp red or white quinoa
  sprouts
salt and pepper

Dressing
2 tbsp lime juice
6 tbsp hazelnut oil
salt and pepper

Method

1 Place the chicken breasts on a board. With the knife parallel to the board, slice each breast in half horizontally to make four fillets.

2 Place the fillets between two sheets of clingfilm and pound with a rolling pin to a thickness of about 8 mm/⅜ inch.

3 Heat the oil in a large frying pan. Add the chicken and fry over a medium–high heat for 3–4 minutes on each side, until golden on the outside and no longer pink in the middle. Transfer to a warmed plate and season to taste with salt and pepper.

4 Slice the chicken lengthways into 2 cm/¾ inch wide strips.

5 Divide the salad leaves between two plates. Arrange the chicken, papaya and avocado on top. Sprinkle with the hazelnuts and quinoa sprouts.

6 To make the dressing, whisk together all the ingredients until smooth and creamy. Pour over the salad and serve immediately.

60 PLUMS

Widely available in many varieties, plums are rich in special phenolic compounds – antioxidants that protect the brain as well as the heart – and compounds beneficial to colon health.

Plums have been much researched because of the health-giving phenolic compounds they contain. These (neochlorogenic and chlorogenic acid) are particularly good at neutralizing the free radicals made in our bodies believed to contribute to disease and the ageing process. Another chemical in plums (hydroxycinnamic acid) is particularly beneficial for the colon and linked with lower risk of colon cancer. Red/purple varieties are also rich in anti-inflammatory anthocyanins and have higher antioxidant levels than yellow plums. Dried or semi-dried plums (or prunes) are a healthy dried fruit snack with concentrated antioxidant power and a high potassium and iron content.

- Rich in phenolic compounds with strong antioxidant action.
- Contain chemicals particularly beneficial for the colon.
- Low-GI rating – useful for slimmers and diabetics.
- Good source of carotenes for protection from cancer and eye health.

Practical tips:
Plums contain their highest levels of antioxidants when fully ripe so don't eat them under-ripe. Cooked plums (halved, stoned and cooked in a little water) will contain almost as many nutrients as when raw – make sure you eat the juice too! Freeze for use in pies, desserts and breakfast compotes.

DID YOU KNOW?

Plums are native to China where they have been eaten for more than 2,000 years. There are over 100 varieties in commercial cultivation.

NUTRIENTS PER MEDIUM-SIZED PLUM

Calories	30
Protein	0.5 mg
Fat	Trace
Carbohydrate	7.5 g
Fibre	0.9 g
Vitamin C	6.3 mg
Potassium	104 mg
Lutein/Zeaxanthin	48 mcg
Beta-carotene	125 mcg

Plum pancakes

SERVES 6

*8 plums, stoned and cut into
    quarters*
100 ml/3½ fl oz maple syrup
1 tbsp lemon juice
1 star anise
200 g/7 oz gluten-free plain flour
*1½ tsp gluten-free baking
    powder*
2 eggs, beaten
*200 ml/7 fl oz sweetened soya
    milk*
100 g/3½ oz natural yogurt
*1 tbsp sunflower oil,
    plus extra for greasing*

Method

1 Place the plums, maple syrup, lemon juice and star anise in a pan
and heat until almost boiling. Reduce the heat, cover and cook
gently for 8–10 minutes, stirring occasionally, until tender.

2 Place the flour, baking powder, eggs, milk, yogurt and oil in a
blender or food processor and blend to a smooth batter.

3 Lightly grease a large, heavy-based frying pan and heat until very
hot. Drop tablespoonfuls of the batter into the pan and cook for
5–6 minutes, turning once, until golden and set. Cook in batches
until all the batter is used up.

4 To serve, stack the pancakes on serving plates and spoon over the
plums and juices.

Vegetables

Whatever flavour, nutrient or colour you want on your plate, there is a vegetable for you. Some are high in starches and so can help boost your carb intake, which is sometimes hard to maintain on a gluten-free diet; most are rich in soluble and insoluble fibre for a healthy digestive system; and all come packed with a huge variety of disease-preventing plant compounds. Folate, magnesium, potassium and iron are just some of the vitamins and minerals that vegetables have in abundance to help you to optimum health.

C High in carbohydrate

F Very good source of fibre

V Rich in vitamins and minerals

D Particularly good for digestive health

P High in protein

N Nutrient boost for gluten-free diet

61 BEETROOTS

Beets are a valuable food for anyone who suffers from digestive problems and intolerances. Food scientists have recently discovered just how rich they are in nutrients and compounds that can help boost our health in several ways.

Beetroot are rich in betaine – a compound that helps improve digestion and nutrient absorption, reduce bloating, calm food intolerances and control yeast and bacterial growth. The nitrates in the root can also raise HDL cholesterol, protect against blood clots and lower high blood pressure significantly for up to 24 hours. Beets are high in the soluble fibre pectin which plays a role in removing toxins from the body and can boost the work of the liver. And studies suggest that beetroot juice may even help increase stamina during aerobic exercise and reduce fatigue.

• Contains betaine to help with several digestive problems.
• Contains nitrates for heart and arterial health.
• Can help increase stamina for exercise.
• A good source of iron, magnesium and vitamins B and C.

Practical tips:
When you cook beets, leave 5 cm/2 inches of stalk and the long 'tail'. This will avoid the beet 'bleeding' and losing colour and nutrients as it cooks. Boil whole until tender or bake brushed with oil. Beetroot can also be eaten raw – peel and grate into winter salads or make a nutritious juice. Use the leaves as you would spinach.

DID YOU KNOW?

Beetroot has a high sugar content for a vegetable but it is released slowly into the body rather than the sudden rush that results from eating sugar.

NUTRIENTS PER MEDIUM-SIZED BEETROOT
(100 g/3½ oz)

Calories	43
Protein	1.6 mg
Fat	Trace
Carbohydrate	9.6 g
Fibre	2.8 g
Folate	109 mcg
Vitamin C	5 mg
Iron	0.8 mg
Magnesium	23 mg
Potassium	325 mg

Spiced beetroot and cucumber tzatziki

SERVES 4

115 g/4 oz cooked beetroot in
    natural juices (drained weight),
    drained and diced
150 g/5½ oz cucumber, diced
40 g/1½ oz radishes, diced
1 spring onion, finely chopped
12 Little Gem lettuce leaves

Dressing

150 g/5½ oz Greek yogurt
¼ tsp ground cumin
½ tsp runny honey
2 tbsp finely chopped fresh mint
salt and pepper

Method

1 To make the dressing, put the yogurt, cumin and honey in a bowl, then stir in the mint and season to taste with salt and pepper.
2 Add the beetroot, cucumber, radishes and spring onion, then toss gently together.
3 Arrange the lettuce leaves on a plate. Spoon a little of the salad into each leaf. Serve immediately.

62 ONIONS

Onions are one of the best vegetables you can eat for your health – they can help combat cancer, heart disease, digestive problems and inflammatory conditions such as arthritis.

The pungent odour and flavour of onions means they're rich in sulphides – compounds that boost immunity to disease, improve cell function and help prevent several common cancers including breast and ovarian cancer. One sulphur compound, onionin A, is unique to onions and has a particularly strong anti-inflammatory effect which may help calm a sensitive gut. Onions are particularly high in the polyphenol quercetin which protects against cardiovascular disease, high cholesterol and cancers (including colon cancer) and is powerfully inflammatory, helping minimize the symptoms of arthritis. Onions are also rich in a type of dietary fibre, called fructo-oligosaccharides, which help maintain a healthy balance of bacteria in the gut, and in vitamin C.

- One of the best sources of polyphenols in the diet.
- Rich in sulphides to protect against cancer.
- Good source of dietary fibre to improve gut health.
- Good source of vitamin C, calcium, potassium and other minerals.

Practical tips:
The flavonoids in onion are mainly in the outer layers so peel off as little as possible and try not to overbrown your onions when sautéing as this destroys the beneficial compounds. Store onions in cool, dry, dark conditions to retain vitamin C.

DID YOU KNOW?

The substance that causes our eyes to stream when we peel an onion is propanethial S-oxide. It can be genetically removed from the vegetable but takes much of the beneficial sulphides with it, so commercial producers leave it in.

NUTRIENTS PER MEDIUM-SIZED ONION (150 G/5½ OZ)

Calories	63
Protein	1.4 mg
Fat	Trace
Carbohydrate	15 g
Fibre	2.1 g
Folate	29 mcg
Vitamin C	9.6 mg
Calcium	33 mg
Magnesium	28 mg
Potassium	216 mg
Selenium	0.8 mcg

Potato and onion frittata

SERVES 4

4 tbsp olive oil

2 large onions, halved and thinly sliced

125 ml/4 fl oz water

50 g/1¾ oz red quinoa, rinsed

700 g/1 lb 9 oz waxy potatoes, peeled, halved lengthways and thinly sliced

9 eggs

½ tsp dried oregano

½ tsp salt

¼ tsp pepper

Method

1 Heat the oil in a frying pan, add the onions and gently fry over a low–medium heat for 25 minutes, until golden and very soft. Drain the onions, reserving the oil.

2 Meanwhile, put the water and quinoa into a small saucepan and bring to the boil. Cover and simmer over a very low heat for 10 minutes, or until most of the liquid has evaporated. Remove from the heat, but leave the pan covered for a further 10 minutes to allow the grains to swell. Fluff up with a fork.

3 While the quinoa is cooking, put the potatoes in a steamer and steam for 8 minutes, until just tender. Spread out to dry on a clean tea towel.

4 In a large bowl, beat the eggs with the oregano, salt and pepper. Add the cooked onions, potatoes and quinoa and stir to combine well.

5 Heat the reserved oil in a deep 25-cm/10-inch non-stick frying pan. Pour in the egg mixture, cover and cook over a low–medium heat for 15 minutes. Meanwhile, preheat the grill.

6 Place the pan under the preheated grill for 5 minutes to finish cooking the top of the frittata. Turn out onto a plate, cut into wedges and serve immediately.

63

PARSNIPS

Low-cost parsnips are often overlooked in the kitchen but they are very nutritious and rich in carbohydrates, making them an ideal alternative to gluten-free grains.

Around 90% of a parsnip's calories are from carbohydrates so they are a good alternative to potatoes or pasta. Parsnips come packed with potassium and folate, two nutrients important for cardiovascular health. Potassium helps protect you from high blood pressure, while folate helps lower your risk of heart disease and helps beat fatigue and weakness. Parsnips are also surprisingly high in vitamin C, supplying about a third of your RDA in a 150-g/5½-oz portion, plus a fifth of your vitamin E needs. Both these antioxidant vitamins help prevent cell damage which can lead to heart disease. The roots also contain useful levels of calcium, iron, magnesium and zinc – four minerals often in short supply in a gluten-free diet.

- Starchy root vegetable with excellent levels of many vitamins and minerals.
- Very high potassium content for cardiovascular health.
- Rich in folate.
- High in the antioxidant vitamins C and E.
- Useful range of minerals ideal for a gluten-free diet.

Practical tips:
Highly versatile, parsnips can be roasted, boiled or steamed, sliced into a gratin with cheese sauce, mashed or made into a soup, and even used instead of potatoes for home-made crisps. Choose medium-sized roots as very large ones may be woody.

DID YOU KNOW?

Parsnips are related to carrots and are ideal to grow over winter, when frosts give the root a superior flavour. In Roman times parsnips were thought to be an aphrodisiac.

NUTRIENTS PER MEDIUM-SIZED PARSNIP (150 G/5½ OZ)

Calories	113
Protein	1.8 g
Fat	0.4 g
Carbohydrate	27 g
Fibre	7.4 g
Folate	101 mcg
Vitamin C	25 mg
Calcium	54 mg
Iron	0.9 mg
Magnesium	44 mg
Potassium	563 mg
Zinc	0.9 mg

Spiced parsnip gratin with ginger cream

SERVES 4

butter, for greasing
3 large parsnips, approx
    750 g/1 lb 10 oz, thinly sliced
425 ml/15 fl oz double cream
250 ml/9 fl oz gluten-free
    vegetable stock
1 garlic clove, crushed
2.5-cm/1-inch piece fresh ginger,
    roughly chopped and crushed
    in a garlic press
¼ tsp white pepper
⅛ tsp freshly grated nutmeg,
    plus extra to garnish
sea salt
snipped fresh chives, to garnish

Method

1 Lightly grease a large gratin dish. Place the parsnips in a steamer set over a saucepan of boiling water. Steam for 3 minutes, until barely tender, shaking halfway through cooking. Tip into the prepared dish and lightly season with salt.

2 Preheat the oven to 180°C/350°F/Gas Mark 4. Gently heat the cream and stock in a saucepan with the garlic and ginger. Do not allow the mixture to boil. Add the pepper, nutmeg and sea salt to taste.

3 Pour the hot cream mixture over the parsnips. Cover the dish with foil and bake in the preheated oven for 20 minutes, with an oven tray underneath to catch any drips.

4 Remove the foil and bake for a further 15–20 minutes, until golden on top.

5 Sprinkle with a little more nutmeg and some chives and serve.

64 POTATOES

Potatoes are very rich in starch and are ideal for boosting the carbohydrate intake of anyone following a gluten-free diet. They also come packed with essential vitamins and minerals.

NUTRIENTS PER MEDIUM-SIZED POTATO WITH SKIN (150 G/5½ OZ)

Calories	104
Protein	2.4 g
Fat	Trace
Carbohydrate	24 g
Fibre	3.6 g
Vitamin B5	0.4 mg
Vitamin B6	0.3 mg
Folate	27 mcg
Niacin	1.6 mg
Vitamin C	30 mg
Iron	0.8 mg
Magnesium	32 mg
Potassium	611 mg

Potatoes are a main source of vitamin C in our diets, containing nearly half of a day's RDA in an average 150-g/5½-oz portion. In addition, they are a particularly good source of the complete range of B vitamins, which work together in our bodies for a healthy nervous system, food digestion and metabolism. Their huge potassium content and their newly discovered content of compounds called kukoamines both work well to lower blood pressure. The tubers also contain useful levels of iron and magnesium. Potato flour is made from cooked, dehydrated and ground potatoes – the flour loses much of the B and C vitamins in the drying process but can be a useful starchy flour mixed with others in gluten-free baking.

- A healthy gluten-free source of starchy carbohydrates.
- Rich in vitamins C and B.
- Potassium and kukoamine content lowers blood pressure.
- Useful source of iron and magnesium.

Practical tips:
Potatoes will give you more fibre if you eat the skins and potatoes cooked in their skin also have a much lower GI (and will keep you feeling fuller for longer) than peeled, mashed potatoes. Depending on the recipe, potato flour may be used as a substitute for wheat flour or as a thickener in casseroles.

Spicy jacket potatoes

SERVES 4

4 baking potatoes,
each about 300 g/10½ oz
1 tbsp vegetable oil (optional)
400 g/14 oz canned chickpeas,
drained and rinsed
1 tsp ground coriander
1 tsp ground cumin
4 tbsp chopped fresh coriander
150 g/5½ oz low-fat natural
yogurt
salt and pepper
salad leaves, to serve

Method

1 Preheat the oven to 200°C/400°F/Gas Mark 6. Scrub the potatoes and pat them dry with absorbent kitchen paper. Prick the potatoes all over with a fork, brush with oil (if using) and season to taste with salt and pepper. Place the potatoes on a baking sheet and bake in the preheated oven for 1–1¼ hours, or until cooked through. Cool for 10 minutes.

2 Meanwhile, place the chickpeas in a large mixing bowl and mash with a fork or potato masher. Stir in the ground coriander, cumin and half the chopped fresh coriander. Cover the bowl with clingfilm and set aside.

3 Halve the cooked potatoes and scoop the flesh into a bowl, keeping the shells intact. Mash the flesh until smooth and gently mix into the chickpea mixture with the yogurt. Season with salt and pepper to taste. Place the potato shells on a baking sheet and fill with the potato and chickpea mixture. Return the potatoes to the oven and bake for 10–15 minutes, until heated through.

4 Garnish the potatoes with the remaining chopped coriander and serve with salad leaves.

65

SWEDE

Swede is one of the lowest-calorie – and cheapest – of all root vegetables but nevertheless it contains several vital nutrients in good amounts.

The typical swede has purple skin and cream-coloured flesh that turns yellow when cooked. This yellow flesh is a good source of carotenes, good for heart health and protecting against cancer. Other important chemicals include glucosinolates, which can also help reduce the risk of getting cancer. Swede contains a good level of vitamin C, with nearly half of your RDA in a 100-g/3½-oz portion. Vitamin C is an immune-boosting and antioxidant vitamin that can help keep skin in good condition. There's also calcium here, for healthy bones and teeth, and potassium. Both these minerals help regulate blood pressure.

- Source of cancer-preventing and heart-protecting carotenes.
- Contains glucosinolates which are also thought to prevent cancers.
- Good source of vitamin C for immune-boosting.
- Provides calcium and potassium.

Practical tips:
Swede is best either cubed and boiled until tender, then mashed with olive or rapeseed oil, or sliced and roasted as you would roast potatoes. The tasty flesh can also be finely chopped and used in a winter soup with kale and onions and is also good mashed half and half with carrot, parsnip or potato, which makes a delicious topping for a cottage pie.

DID YOU KNOW?

When swede was first cultivated, it was known as the turnip-rooted cabbage (it is a member of the brassica family). In 1780, Sweden introduced the vegetable into the UK, hence the name (except in Scotland, where it is called 'neep').

NUTRIENTS PER 100 G/3½ oz SWEDE

Calories	24
Protein	0.7 g
Fat	0.3 g
Carbohydrate	5 g
Fibre	1.9 g
Folate	31 mcg
Niacin	1.2 mg
Vitamin C	31 mg
Calcium	53 mg
Potassium	170 mg
Carotenes	350 mcg

Roasted root vegetables with garlic

SERVES 4

300 g/10½ oz swede
2 large carrots
2 parsnips
300 g/10½ oz waxy potatoes
1 large red onion, sliced
8 large garlic cloves, unpeeled
1 tsp ground cumin
1 tsp ground coriander
3 tbsp olive or
  rapeseed oil
100 ml/3½ fl oz gluten-free
  vegetable stock
1 tbsp lemon juice
½ tbsp runny honey
salt and pepper

Method

1 Preheat the oven to 190°C/375°F/Gas Mark 5. Peel all the vegetables. Cut the swede, carrots and parsnips into thick fingers and slice the potato into 5-mm/¼-inch thick rounds.

2 Place all the vegetables in a large roasting tin. Add the garlic, spices, salt and pepper to taste and the oil and toss together until combined. Spread the vegetables out until they cover the base of the tin. Place in the preheated oven and roast for 25 minutes.

3 Remove the tin from the oven and turn all the vegetables over using a fish slice. Combine the stock, lemon juice and honey and sprinkle over the vegetables, then return to the oven for 15 minutes, or until only a little liquid remains and the vegetables are golden and tender. Serve immediately.

66 SWEET POTATOES

Packed with nutrients, sweet potatoes are also rich in starches that can help regulate blood sugars, so they are an excellent food to include in a gluten-free diet.

Sweet potatoes are richer in nutrients than traditional potatoes and can be substituted for them in many recipes. They have a lower GI than potatoes and also, unusually, help boost blood levels of adiponectin, a hormone that helps regulate insulin in diabetics. They also contain plant sterols and pectin, both of which help lower LDL blood cholesterol. Sweet potatoes are also one of the best food sources of beta-carotene, which is antioxidant, anti-cancer and helps boost the immune system. In addition, these super-tubers are an excellent source of antioxidant vitamins and minerals including vitamin E and magnesium, and the antioxidant protein, sporamin.

- Very rich content of carotenes with strong anti-cancer action.
- Sterols and pectin content helps reduce LDL cholesterol.
- Low-GI and with ability to stabilize insulin, useful for diabetics.
- Antioxidant minerals and vitamin E to protect skin.

Practical tips:
Choose small to medium-sized sweet potatoes with unmarked skins as these will be more tender when cooked. Bake or roast as normal potatoes, or mash with a little oil (fat helps the body absorb carotene). Unlike potatoes, the skins are rather tough and chewy, so you may prefer to peel them off. Sweet potatoes are excellent in curries, soups and casseroles.

DID YOU KNOW?

Sweet potatoes are often confused with yams but are not related at all. White-fleshed yams, related to the lily, contain fewer nutrients and taste drier and less creamy than sweet potatoes, which are from the convolvulus family.

NUTRIENTS PER MEDIUM-SIZED SWEET POTATO
(150 g/5½ oz)

Calories	129
Protein	2.4 g
Fat	Trace
Carbohydrate	30.2 g
Fibre	4.5 g
Vitamin C	3.6 mg
Vitamin E	0.4 mg
Calcium	45 mg
Iron	0.9 mg
Magnesium	38 mg
Potassium	506 mg
Zinc	0.5 mg
Beta-carotene	12,760 mcg

Spicy sweet potato chips

SERVES 6

900 g/2 lb sweet potatoes
2 tbsp vegetable oil,
  plus extra for greasing
½ tsp salt
½ tsp ground cumin
¼ tsp cayenne pepper

Method

1 Preheat the oven to 230°C/450°F/Gas Mark 8. Grease a large baking tray.

2 Peel the sweet potatoes and slice into 5-mm/¼-inch thick spears about 7.5 cm/3 inches long. Spread the sweet potatoes on the prepared baking tray and drizzle with the oil.

3 In a small bowl, combine the salt, cumin and cayenne. Sprinkle the spice mixture evenly over the sweet potatoes and then toss to coat.

4 Spread the sweet potatoes out into a single layer and bake in the preheated oven for about 15–20 minutes, or until cooked through and lightly coloured. Serve immediately.

67 BROAD BEANS

Broad beans have an almost perfect balance of carbohydrate and protein and are ideal for boosting your gluten-free carbohydrate intake for the day.

Broad beans are an excellent vegetable source of protein and starch and so make a very satisfying side dish or part of a main meal to boost your carb intake. These beans, however, have much more to recommend them. They are particularly high in dietary fibre and exceptionally high in a form of soluble fibre called arabinose, which can help improve the blood lipid profile and reduce blood LDL cholesterol. They have a very good level of vitamin C with all its antioxidant benefits. Broad beans are also rich in a range of minerals from iron (which is vital to transport oxygen throughout our bodies) to magnesium and calcium (for healthy bones) and zinc (to boost the immune system).

- Very good source of vegetable protein.
- Starchy vegetable helps boost carbohydrate intake.
- Rich in iron for healthy blood.
- A good source of calcium for bones.

Practical tips:
Broad beans are best eaten when young and tender – they retain most nutrients if the outer pale green shell of the individual beans is intact but you can also slip this skin off and eat the bright green beans inside. They go very well with fresh summer herbs, such as mint and parsley, and with lemon, bacon and chicken. Alternatively, try them puréed with garlic to make a bean hummus.

DID YOU KNOW?

Broad beans originated in the Middle East and are widely eaten there today, often dried as fava beans.

NUTRIENTS PER 100 G/3½ OZ SHELLED BROAD BEANS

Calories	81
Protein	8 g
Fat	0.6 g
Carbohydrate	11.7 g
Fibre	6.5 g
Vitamin C	8 mg
Calcium	56 mg
Iron	1.6 mg
Magnesium	36 mg
Potassium	280 mg
Zinc	1 mg

Chilled broad bean soup

SERVES 6

*850 ml/1½ pints gluten-free
  vegetable stock*
*650 g/1 lb 7 oz shelled fresh
  young broad beans*
3 tbsp lemon juice
*2 tbsp chopped fresh summer
  savory*
salt and pepper
6 tbsp Greek yogurt, to serve
chopped fresh mint, to garnish

Method

1 Pour the stock into a large saucepan and bring to the boil. Reduce the heat to a simmer, add the broad beans and cook for about 7 minutes, or until the beans are tender.

2 Remove the pan from the heat and leave to cool slightly. Transfer to a food processor or blender, in batches if necessary, and process until smooth. Push the mixture through a strainer set over a bowl.

3 Stir in the lemon juice and summer savory and season to taste with salt and pepper. Leave to cool completely, then cover with clingfilm and chill in the refrigerator for at least 3 hours.

4 To serve, ladle into chilled bowls or glasses, top each with a tablespoon of yogurt and garnish with mint. Serve immediately.

68

PEAS

Either freshly picked or frozen, peas are a versatile and rich source of vitamin C and several other important nutrients and plant chemicals, including soluble fibre to help digestion.

DID YOU KNOW?

Frozen peas can often contain more vitamin C and other nutrients than fresh peas because they are frozen within hours of picking to retain nutrients. Shop-bought peas in their pods may be several days old.

NUTRIENTS PER 100 G/3½ OZ SHELLED PEAS

Calories	81
Protein	5.4 g
Fat	0.4 g
Carbohydrate	14.5 g
Fibre	5.1 g
Folate	65 mcg
Niacin	2.1 mg
Vitamin C	40 mg
Calcium	25 mg
Iron	1.5 mg
Magnesium	33 mg
Potassium	244 mg
Zinc	1.2 mg
Lutein/Zeaxanthin	2477 mcg
Beta-carotene	450 mcg

Peas contain more protein than most vegetables and have a very high fibre content, including the soluble fibre pectin to aid digestion and lower LDL blood cholesterol. They are particularly high in vitamin C, a heart-protective antioxidant, and in the B vitamins folate and niacin. They are also rich in the carotenoids lutein/zeaxanthin (for healthy eyes) and high in all the major minerals (calcium, iron, magnesium and zinc) which can be lacking on a gluten-free diet. And these little nutrient stores are packed with several anti-inflammatory, anti-cancer and anti-diabetes chemicals including pisumsaponins and pisomosides that are found almost exclusively in peas.

- Rich in fibre and soluble fibre for digestive and artery health.
- High in antioxidants including vitamin C.
- Contain a great range of important minerals.
- Packed with disease-preventing phytochemicals.

Practical tips:

Buy peas in the pod young – as they age the sugars turn to starch and give them a mealy texture and flavour. Young pods (mangetout or sugar snap peas) can be eaten with the immature peas inside. Eat young, small peas raw to glean the most vitamin C. To cook peas, steam lightly or boil in as little water as possible (vitamin C content leaches into water during cooking).

Peas with lettuce

SERVES 4–6

30 g/1 oz butter, plus an
   extra knob
1 tsp sunflower oil
30 g/1 oz unsmoked lardons
1 shallot, finely chopped
280 g/10 oz shelled peas
300 ml/10 fl oz gluten-free
   vegetable stock or water
1 Little Gem lettuce,
   cored and shredded
2 tbsp chopped fresh chervil
salt and pepper

Method

1 Melt the butter with the oil in a large saucepan over a medium heat. Add the lardons and stir for 3 minutes. Add the shallot and continue frying for a further 3 minutes.

2 Add the peas and stock and season to taste with salt and pepper (but remember that the lardons are very salty). Cover the pan and bring to the boil over a high heat, then uncover, reduce the heat slightly and simmer for 5 minutes.

3 Add the lettuce and continue to simmer, uncovered, until the peas are tender and the liquid has evaporated. Stir in a knob of butter, then taste and adjust the seasoning, if necessary. Stir in the chervil and serve immediately.

69 TOMATOES

Tasty tomatoes have plenty to offer nutritionally and can help protect us from cardiovascular disease and cancer.

Tomatoes are packed with carotenes, particularly lycopene which is strongly linked with protection from prostate cancer (one of the most common cancers in men), and boosting heart health. Tomatoes are also rich in salicylates which have an anti-blood clotting effect. Several other antioxidants, including vitamin C, quercetin and lutein are found in tomatoes in good amounts. They are low in calories but high in potassium, which helps to regulate blood pressure and body fluids, and they contain useful amounts of dietary fibre. Kaempferol and anti-bacterial glycosides found in tomatoes may help lessen gut sensitivity.

- Excellent source of lycopene to protect against prostate cancer.
- Rich in potassium to help regulate blood pressure and prevent fluid retention.
- Great source of antioxidants such as quercetin, lutein and vitamin C.
- Contain salicylates which have an anti-blood clotting effect.

Practical tips:
Tomatoes ripened on the vine contain more lycopene than those ripened after picking and it is better absorbed when eaten with some oil as a salad dressing or with olive oil for cooking. Lycopene is also more active in processed tomato products such as ketchup, tomato purée and tomato juice than it is in raw tomatoes. The skin contains more antioxidants than the flesh, while the seeds are high in salicylates. Remove raw tomatoes from the refrigerator an hour before serving for the best flavour.

DID YOU KNOW?

Often thought of as a vegetable but actually a fruit, tomatoes are one of our most popular foods and come from the same 'nightshade' family as potatoes and aubergines.

NUTRIENTS PER 100 G/3½ oz TOMATO

Calories	18
Protein	0.9 g
Fat	0.2 g
Carbohydrate	3.9 g
Fibre	1.2 g
Vitamin C	13.7 mg
Vitamin E	0.5 mg
Potassium	237 mg
Lutein/Zeaxanthin	123 mcg
Lycopene	2537 mcg

Meatballs with tomato sauce

SERVES 4

800 g/1 lb 12 oz canned
    chopped tomatoes
5 garlic cloves, crushed
2 tsp dried oregano
150 ml/5 fl oz olive oil
½ tsp salt
chopped fresh flat-leaf parsley
    and freshly grated Parmesan
    cheese, to serve

Meatballs

1 small onion, grated
finely grated rind of 1 large
    lemon
2 garlic cloves, crushed
2 tsp dried oregano
1 tsp salt
¾ tsp pepper
1 large egg white, lightly beaten
500 g/1 lb 2 oz fresh pork mince
250 g/9 oz fresh beef mince
4 tbsp milled chia seeds

Method

1 First, make the meatballs. In a small bowl mix together the onion, lemon rind, garlic and oregano with the salt, pepper and egg white.

2 Combine the pork and beef in a large bowl. Add the egg white mixture and use a fork to mix together well. Mix in the chia seeds and leave to stand.

3 Meanwhile, put the tomatoes into a large pan with the garlic and oregano, 4 tablespoons of the oil and the salt. Bring to the boil, then simmer briskly, uncovered, for 30 minutes, until thickened.

4 Divide the meat mixture into 20 balls, rolling them in the palm of your hand until firm.

5 Heat the remaining oil in a large frying pan. Add the meatballs and fry for about 8 minutes, turning frequently, until brown all over. Transfer to kitchen paper to drain, then add to the tomato sauce and simmer for 5 minutes.

6 Transfer the meatballs and sauce to plates, sprinkle with parsley and serve with Parmesan.

70 AUBERGINE

A glossy, purple aubergine is not only attractive but also contains a feast of different vitamins and minerals, as well as plant chemicals to boost brainpower.

Aubergines contain several antioxidant compounds including one interesting flavonoid called nasunin. This helps to protect brain cells, particularly the fatty cells, from damage and may help boost brainpower and memory. The vegetable also contains terpenes which can relax the blood vessels and may offer protection against high blood pressure and high cholesterol. The very high potassium levels will help to boost that effect. A third of the vegetable's extremely high fibre content is in the form of soluble fibre which helps slow down the rate of food digestion and is helpful for anyone with a sensitive gut. Aubergines also contain magnesium, calcium, vitamin C, folate and vitamin E.

• Fibre content aids good digestion.
• Contains the flavonoid nasunin which may boost brain function.
• Terpenes and potassium protect against heart and arterial disease.
• Good range of vitamins and minerals.

Practical tips:
Most commercially grown aubergines no longer have a slightly bitter taste so it's not necessary to salt them before use. Cut aubergines turn brown quickly and spoil, so don't slice until you need to cook them. The fruits soak up a lot of fat if fried, so grill or bake instead. Simply brush the pieces with oil beforehand.

NUTRIENTS PER HALF MEDIUM-SIZED AUBERGINE (225 G/8 oz)

Calories	55
Protein	2.3 g
Fat	0.4 g
Carbohydrate	13 g
Fibre	7.8 g
Folate	50 mcg
Vitamin C	5 mg
Vitamin E	0.7 mg
Calcium	21 mg
Magnesium	32 mg
Potassium	527 mg

Aubergine tagine with polenta

SERVES 4

1 aubergine, diced
3 tbsp olive oil
1 large onion, thinly sliced
1 carrot, diced
2 garlic cloves, chopped
115 g/4 oz mushrooms, sliced
2 tsp ground coriander
2 tsp cumin seeds
1 tsp chilli powder
1 tsp ground turmeric
600 g/1 lb 5 oz canned chopped
    tomatoes
300 ml/10 fl oz gluten-free
    vegetable stock
70 g/2½ oz dried apricots,
    chopped
400 g/14 oz canned chickpeas,
    drained and rinsed
2 tbsp chopped fresh coriander,
    to garnish

Polenta
1.2 litres/2 pints hot gluten-free
    vegetable stock
200 g/7 oz quick-cook polenta

Method

1 Preheat the grill to medium. Toss the aubergine in 1 tablespoon of the oil and arrange in the grill pan. Cook under the preheated grill for 20 minutes, turning occasionally, until softened and beginning to blacken around the edges – brush with more oil if the slices become too dry.

2 Heat the remaining oil in a large, heavy-based saucepan over a medium heat. Add the onion and fry, stirring occasionally, for 8 minutes, or until soft and golden. Add the carrot, garlic and mushrooms and cook for 5 minutes. Add the spices and cook, stirring constantly, for a further minute.

3 Add the tomatoes and stock, stir well and bring to the boil. Reduce the heat and simmer for 10 minutes, or until the sauce begins to thicken and reduce.

4 Add the grilled aubergine, the apricots and chickpeas, partially cover and cook for a further 10 minutes, stirring occasionally.

5 Meanwhile, to make the polenta, pour the hot stock into a large saucepan and bring to the boil. Pour in the polenta in a steady stream, stirring constantly with a wooden spoon. Reduce the heat to low and cook for 1–2 minutes, or until the polenta thickens to a mashed potato-like consistency. Serve the tagine with the polenta, sprinkled with the fresh coriander.

71

PEPPERS

Richly-coloured, sweet bell peppers contain high levels of carotenes for heart health and cancer protection, are full of vitamin C and are a good source of folate, which are often low in a gluten-free diet.

Sweet peppers come in a variety of colours, but the purple, red and orange peppers contain the highest levels of anti-cancer and heart protective carotenes and are one of the best vegetable sources of these chemicals. They are particularly rich in eye-protective lutein and zeaxanthin and in immune-boosting cryptoxanthin, an easily-absorbed form of carotene. All colours of peppers are extremely rich in vitamin C with a 100-g/3½-oz serving providing almost twice a day's recommended intake. They are also a good source of the B vitamin folate and a useful source of vitamin E, both of which can be lacking in a gluten-free diet.

- Contain several phytochemicals which are strongly anti-cancer and immune-boosting.
- Very good source of a range of vitamins and minerals.
- Extremely rich in antioxidant vitamin C.
- High lutein/zeaxanthin levels protect eyesight.

Practical tips:
Either cook peppers with some oil or use them raw in a salad dressed with oil as the carotenes are better absorbed in our bodies when eaten with fat. Fresh peppers freeze well (slice and bag beforehand) for use in cooking and are also good blended into a vegetable smoothie.

DID YOU KNOW?

Peppers have recently been found to contain small amounts of nicotine which researchers have found can help reduce the risk of Parkinson's disease without the drawbacks of smoking.

NUTRIENTS PER 100 G/3½ OZ RED PEPPER

Calories	31
Protein	1 g
Fat	0.3 g
Carbohydrate	6 g
Fibre	2.1 g
Vitamin B6	0.3 mg
Folate	46 mcg
Vitamin C	128 mg
Vitamin E	1.58 mg
Potassium	211 mg
Cryptoxanthin	735 mcg
Lutein/Zeaxanthin	77 mcg
Beta-carotene	2436 mcg

Roasted pepper salad

SERVES 4

2 red peppers, halved and
    deseeded
2 yellow peppers, halved and
    deseeded
1 red onion, roughly chopped
2 garlic cloves, finely chopped
6 tbsp olive oil
100 g/3½ oz mini mozzarella
    cheese pearls, drained
2 tbsp roughly torn
    fresh basil
2 tbsp balsamic vinegar
salt and pepper

Method

1 Preheat the oven to 190°C/375°F/Gas Mark 5. Put the peppers
cut-side up in a shallow roasting tin. Scatter over the onion
and garlic, season well with salt and pepper and drizzle over
3 tablespoons of the olive oil. Roast for 40 minutes, or until
the peppers are tender. Leave to cool.

2 Arrange the cold peppers in a serving dish and pour over any juices
left in the roasting tin. Scatter over the mozzarella and basil.

3 To make the dressing, whisk together the remaining olive oil and the
balsamic vinegar, then drizzle over the peppers. Cover and leave to
marinate in the refrigerator for at least 2 hours before serving.

72 FENNEL

Fennel bulbs are high in nutrients that aid digestion, reduce inflammation and can help to prevent some cancers. This is a particularly useful vegetable for anyone with a gluten intolerance.

Fennel contains a strong combination of plant chemicals, including the flavonoids rutin, quercetin and kaempferol, all of which give it strong antioxidant activity. Its natural compounds are known to help calm the digestive system, helping to eliminate or ease flatulence, colic and indigestion. One of the compounds in fennel, anethole, has also been shown to reduce inflammation and to help prevent the occurrence of cancer. It is also a very good source of dietary fibre and calcium and contains a wide range of other nutrients including vitamin C, folate and iron. The very high potassium content means that fennel is a diuretic, helping to eliminate surplus fluid from the body.

- Range of antioxidants for general health protection.
- Diuretic and digestive aid.
- Anti-inflammatory and anti-cancer.
- Good source of a range of vitamins and minerals.

Practical tips:
Florence (or Italian) fennel has a refreshing, slightly sweet, liquorice flavour. All parts are edible – cut off the root end and peel away any tough outer skin. The stems are tough and stringy so use these to make soup. Fennel goes particularly well with chicken and fish – try baking small whole fish in foil on a bed of thinly sliced fennel. Roast or steam wedges of the bulb, or braise sautéed slices in a little vegetable stock. It is also delicious raw – thinly slice into salads.

DID YOU KNOW?

Florence fennel is related to parsley, carrots, dill and coriander. It is also closely related to the herb fennel and the leafy tops of the bulb can be washed, chopped and used as a garnish.

NUTRIENTS PER SMALL FENNEL BULB (100 G/3½ OZ)

Calories	31
Protein	1.2 g
Fat	0.2 g
Carbohydrate	7.3 g
Fibre	3.1 g
Folate	27 mcg
Vitamin C	12 mg
Calcium	4.9 mg
Iron	0.7 mg
Potassium	414 mg

Quinoa salad with fennel and orange

SERVES 4

900 ml/1½ pints gluten-free
vegetable stock
225 g/8 oz white quinoa, rinsed
and drained
3 oranges
250 g/9 oz fennel bulbs, very
thinly sliced, green
feathery tops reserved and
torn into small pieces
2 spring onions, finely chopped
15 g/½ oz fresh flat-leaf
parsley, roughly chopped

Dressing
juice of ½ lemon
3 tbsp olive oil
pepper

Method

1 Bring the stock to the boil in a saucepan, add the quinoa and
simmer for 10–12 minutes, or until the germs separate from the
seeds. Drain off the stock and discard, then spoon the quinoa into
a salad bowl and leave to cool.

2 Grate the rind from two of the oranges and put it in a clean jam jar.
Cut a slice off the top and bottom of each of the three oranges,
then remove the peel in thin vertical slices and discard. Cut
between the membranes to remove the orange segments, then
squeeze the juice from the membranes into the jam jar.

3 Add the orange segments, fennel slices, spring onions and parsley
to the quinoa in the salad bowl.

4 To make the dressing, add the lemon juice and oil to the jam jar,
season to taste with pepper, screw on the lid and shake well.
Drizzle over the salad and toss everything together. Garnish with the
fennel fronds and serve immediately.

73

BUTTERNUT SQUASH

Butternut squash is one of the best sources of health-boosting carotenes. These powerful plant compounds help to keep skin in good condition and protect us from cancer and other diseases.

The orange-fleshed varieties of squash, including butternut, contain the highest levels of beneficial carotenes – one of these, beta-cryptoxanthin, is linked with protection from lung cancer. Squash is also one of the best sources of lutein and zeaxanthin, the carotenes associated with good eyesight, particularly in older age. Carotenes can also help reduce the inflammation associated with arthritis and arterial disease and lower the risk of colon and prostate cancers. Butternut squash is also a very good source of antioxidant vitamins C and E. The essential minerals calcium, iron and magnesium are all here in good amounts to keep bones strong and help keep fatigue at bay.

- Contains carotenes that are known to give us protection from many types of cancer.
- Rich in compounds that protect ageing eyesight.
- Helps reduce inflammation and the symptoms of arthritis.
- Good source of antioxidant vitamins C and E.

Practical tips:
Squashes have a smooth texture and nutty flavour ideal for both sweet and savoury dishes. They go particularly well with chicken and beef. Your body will absorb the carotenes better if you eat squash with a little oil, so roast cubes in olive oil or steam and dress with oil. Add roasted cubes to soups, vegetable chillies and curries.

DID YOU KNOW?

Squash seeds are packed with nutrients. Wash them thoroughly and dry naturally or spread on a baking sheet, sprinkle with a little olive oil and roast for 15 minutes at a low temperature for a nutritious snack.

NUTRIENTS PER 150 G/5½ OZ BUTTERNUT SQUASH

Calories	68
Protein	1.5 g
Fat	Trace
Carbohydrate	7.5 g
Fibre	3 g
Folate	41 mcg
Niacin	1.8 mg
Vitamin C	31 mg
Vitamin E	2.2 mg
Calcium	72 mg
Iron	1 mg
Magnesium	51 mg
Potassium	528 mg
Beta-carotene	6339 mcg

Butternut squash stew

SERVES 4

1 tbsp olive oil
1 onion, diced
3 garlic cloves, finely chopped
2 tbsp tomato purée
2 tsp ground cumin
1 tsp ground cinnamon
1 tsp salt
¼ tsp cayenne pepper
450 g/1 lb butternut squash,
  peeled, deseeded and cut
  into bite-sized pieces
100 g/3½ oz brown lentils
450 ml/15 fl oz gluten-free
  vegetable stock
1 tbsp lemon juice

To garnish
4 tbsp natural yogurt
2 tbsp finely chopped fresh
  coriander
2 tbsp flaked almonds

Method

1 Heat the oil in a large saucepan over a medium–high heat. Add the onion and garlic and cook, stirring occasionally, for about 5 minutes, or until soft.

2 Add the tomato purée, cumin, cinnamon, salt and cayenne and give it a quick stir. Add the squash, lentils and stock and bring to the boil. Reduce the heat to low and simmer, uncovered, stirring occasionally, for about 25 minutes, until the squash and lentils are tender.

3 Just before serving, stir in the lemon juice. Serve hot, garnished with a dollop of the yogurt and a sprinkling of coriander and flaked almonds.

74 BROCCOLI

Broccoli contains a huge range of vitamins, minerals and plant compounds that provide many health benefits and is a good source of fibre.

All types of broccoli – calabrese, purple sprouting and tenderstem types – are rich in phytonutrients but the dark green and purple varieties have the highest levels. Broccoli contains sulphoraphane, indoles, selenium and immune-boosting vitamin C, all of which offer protection against breast and other forms of cancer. The vegetable is also rich in carotenes, which help to lower LDL cholesterol and protect against heart disease, and may also help improve memory and dry skin. Lutein and zeaxanthin found here protect eye health and vision, and broccoli is also one of the best vegetable sources of calcium to protect against osteoporosis.

- Contains sulphoraphane and other nutrients for strong protection against cancer and heart disease.
- Carotenes protect against heart disease and may improve memory and skin.
- High calcium content helps build and protect bones.

Practical tips:
Three 80-g/2¾-oz servings of broccoli a week will give you optimum protection against cancer. Lightly steam or stir-fry to get the most vitamin C and antioxidants from the vegetable, and don't forget the leaves and the stalks – these are also edible and are full of fibre. Try instead of cauliflower for a tasty broccoli cheese bake.

DID YOU KNOW?

Sulphoraphane, found in broccoli, also appears to help protect against peptic ulcers by killing the bacteria that cause them.

NUTRIENTS PER 100 G/3½ oz BROCCOLI

Calories	34
Protein	2.8 g
Fat	0.4 g
Carbohydrate	6.6 g
Fibre	2.6 g
Vitamin C	89 mg
Calcium	47 mg
Selenium	2.5 mcg
Lutein/Zeaxanthin	1403 mcg
Beta-carotene	361 mcg

Buckwheat noodle and broccoli salad

SERVES 4

150 g/5½ oz gluten-free soba (buckwheat) noodles

200 g/7 oz frozen edamame beans

225 g/8 oz broccoli, cut into small florets, stems thinly sliced

1 red pepper, halved, deseeded and thinly sliced

1 purple or orange pepper, halved, deseeded and thinly sliced

115 g/4 oz chestnut mushrooms, thinly sliced

85 g/3 oz ready-to-eat sprouting sunflower seeds

Dressing

2 tbsp rice vinegar

2 tbsp gluten-free tamari (Japanese soy sauce)

4 tbsp rice bran oil

4-cm/1½-inch piece of fresh ginger, peeled and finely grated

Method

1 Put cold water in the base of a steamer, bring to the boil, then add the noodles and frozen edamame beans and bring back to the boil. Put the broccoli in the top of the steamer, then put it on the steamer base, cover and steam for 3–5 minutes, or until the noodles and vegetables are just tender. Drain and rinse the noodles and edamame beans, then drain again and tip into a salad bowl. Add the broccoli, then leave to cool.

2 To make the dressing, put the vinegar, tamari, oil and ginger in a clean jam jar, screw on the lid and shake well. Drizzle over the salad and toss gently together.

3 Add the peppers and mushrooms to the salad and toss again. Spoon into four bowls, then top with the sprouting seeds and serve immediately.

75 RED CABBAGE

This firm, purple-red cabbage is packed with a good range of phytochemicals for general health protection and many nutrients for digestive health.

Red cabbage is rich in compounds that protect us from disease. These include indoles, which have been linked to protection from breast, uterus and ovarian cancers and can help protect against the signs of ageing. It also contains sulphoraphane, which can help block cancer-causing chemicals, and monoterpenes, which protect body cells from damage by free radicals. Red cabbage is much higher than other cabbages in carotenes including lycopene, which offers protection from prostate cancer, and the glucosinolates, glutamine and polyphenols found here appear to protect the lining of the intestines against attack from harmful bacteria and from ulcers. The purply leaves also contain anthocyanins, which may help prevent Alzheimer's disease. Additional benefits of eating red cabbage are the good levels of vitamin C and minerals, including calcium and selenium.

- Contains a variety of cancer-fighting compounds.
- Low in calories and ideal for slimmers.
- Rich in the antioxidant vitamin C and several minerals.
- Anthocyanin content may protect against Alzheimer's disease.

Practical tips:
Red cabbage is an ideal ingredient for a coleslaw, with white cabbage and carrot. Alternatively, try it braised with chopped onion, apple, vinegar and honey – delicious with roast pork or lamb. Store wrapped in the refrigerator to retain its vitamin C content.

DID YOU KNOW?

The juice from red cabbage leaves can be used as a natural dye. It is also an antiseptic – useful to dab on any cuts that happen in the kitchen.

NUTRIENTS PER 100 G/3½ oz RED CABBAGE

Calories	31
Protein	1.4 g
Fat	Trace
Carbohydrate	7.4 g
Fibre	2.1 g
Folate	18 mcg
Niacin	0.4 mg
Vitamin C	57 mg
Calcium	45 mg
Iron	0.8 mg
Potassium	243 mcg
Selenium	0.6 mcg
Lutein/Zeaxanthin	329 mcg
Beta-carotene	670 mcg

Red cabbage salad with aubergine dip

SERVES 4

2 carrots
350 g/12 oz red cabbage,
   shredded
55 g/2 oz raisins
125 g/4½ oz bistro salad, a mix
   of red-stemmed baby red
   chard, bull's blood chard and
   lamb's lettuce
juice of 1 orange
pepper

Dip
3 aubergines
3 garlic cloves, finely chopped
2 tbsp tahini
3 tbsp hemp oil
pepper

Method

1 To make the dip, preheat the grill to high and remove the grill rack. Prick both ends of each aubergine with a fork, put them in the grill pan and grill 5 cm/2 inches away from the heat source, turning several times, for 15–20 minutes, until blackened. Leave to cool.

2 Shave the carrots into long, thin ribbons using a swivel-bladed vegetable peeler, then put them on a serving plate. Add the cabbage, then sprinkle over the raisins and salad leaves. Drizzle with the orange juice and season with a little pepper.

3 Cut the aubergines in half and scoop the soft flesh away from the blackened skins using a dessertspoon. Finely chop the flesh, then put it in a bowl. Add the garlic, tahini and hemp oil, season with a little pepper and mix together. Spoon into a serving bowl and nestle in the centre of the salad to serve.

76 KALE

Curly kale is one of the best leafy greens to eat regularly – it contains the highest levels of antioxidants of all vegetables.

The dark green leaves contain various plant chemicals known for their anti-ageing properties and disease-fighting abilities. These include flavonoids, to lower LDL cholesterol, and indoles and isothiocyanates to protect against colon, bladder, breast and prostate cancers. Kale is unusually rich in vitamins and minerals – a 100-g/3½-oz portion contains almost twice the RDA of vitamin C, which helps the body absorb the vegetable's high iron content. A similar sized portion also gives around a sixth of our daily calcium needs and is a good source of selenium, which helps fight cancer, and magnesium and vitamin E, which are important for heart health. The vitamin E and carotenes in kale also keep skin and eyes healthy. Kale also contains small amounts of anti-inflammatory omega-3 fats.

- Extremely high in vitamin C.
- Rich in flavonoids, indoles and antioxidants to fight heart disease and cancers.
- Contains more calcium and iron than any other vegetable.
- Extremely rich in carotenes to protect eyes and help prevent cataracts.

Practical tips:
Store kale in a plastic bag in the refrigerator to prevent it from wilting. The outer, deepest green leaves contain the most carotenes and indoles. Steam or stir-fry then leave to rest for a few minutes to maximize the potency of the antioxidants. Kale's strong, iron flavour marries well with beef, bacon, pasta and potato, and is delicious in vegetable soups.

DID YOU KNOW?

Kale is a great winter vegetable and becomes sweeter to eat once it has been through a winter frost.

NUTRIENTS PER 100 G/3½ oz KALE

Calories	50
Protein	3.3 g
Fat	0.7 g
Carbohydrate	10 g
Fibre	2 g
Folate	29 mcg
Vitamin C	120 mg
Vitamin E	1.7 mg
Calcium	135 mg
Iron	1.7 mg
Magnesium	34 mg
Potassium	447 mg
Selenium	0.9 mcg
Lutein/Zeaxanthin	39,550 mcg
Beta-carotene	9226 mcg

Kale and butter bean casserole

SERVES 6

*350 g/12 oz butter beans,
    soaked overnight*
1 tbsp cumin seeds
2 tsp dried oregano
3 tbsp groundnut oil
2 onions, chopped
2 garlic cloves, thinly sliced
*1–3 fresh red or green chillies,
    deseeded and sliced*
*400 g/14 oz canned chopped
    tomatoes*
*450 ml/15 fl oz gluten-free
    vegetable stock*
175 g/6 oz shredded kale
5 tbsp chopped fresh coriander
juice of 1 lime
salt and pepper
*2 avocados, cubed and tossed
    with lime juice, and red onion
    slivers, to garnish*

Method

1 Drain the beans, put them into a large saucepan and cover with water. Bring to the boil, boil rapidly for 15 minutes, then reduce the heat and simmer for 30–45 minutes, until tender but not disintegrating. Drain and set aside.

2 Put the cumin seeds into a small dry frying pan over a medium heat and fry until fragrant. Add the oregano, fry for a few seconds, then immediately remove the mixture from the pan.

3 Lightly crush the mixture in a mortar with a pestle.

4 Heat the oil in a large, flameproof casserole over a medium heat. Add the chopped onions and the spice and herb mixture. Fry for 5 minutes, until the onions are translucent. Add the garlic and chillies and fry for a further 2 minutes.

5 Stir in the tomatoes, beans and stock. Season with salt and pepper and bring to the boil. Reduce the heat, cover and simmer for 30 minutes, stirring occasionally.

6 Increase the heat and stir in the kale. Simmer, uncovered, for 7 minutes, or until tender but still brightly coloured. Stir in the coriander and lime juice.

7 Ladle into soup plates, garnish with the avocado and red onion and serve immediately.

77 SPINACH

The strong iron taste of spinach gives a hint that this vegetable packs a punch in the nutrition department. New research also shows that it contains anti-inflammatory compounds that may help protect your digestive system.

Researchers have found many flavonoid compounds in spinach that act as antioxidants and fight against stomach, skin, breast, prostate and other cancers. Spinach is also extremely high in carotenes, which protect eyesight, and is particularly rich in vitamin K, which helps to boost bone strength and may help prevent osteoporosis. It also contains peptides which have been shown to lower blood pressure. The relatively high vitamin E present may help protect brainpower and memory as we age, while the extremely high amount of folate in spinach offers protection against heart problems, cancers and birth defects. Spinach is also very rich in potassium, magnesium and iron.

- Flavonoid and carotene content protects against many cancers.
- Vitamin C, folate and carotenes help maintain heart health.
- Vitamin K and magnesium – important for bone health.
- Extremely rich source of minerals.

Practical tips:

Try to eat spinach with oil to help your body absorb the beneficial carotenes – try stir-frying, drizzle oil over wilted spinach, or add an olive oil and lemon dressing to raw baby leaves. Boost iron absorption by adding plenty of vitamin C-rich foods to your plate.

DID YOU KNOW?

Although spinach is rich in calcium, our bodies are unable to absorb most of it due to the oxalates in the leaves that inhibit this. However, these oxalates don't appear to adversely affect iron absorption.

NUTRIENTS PER 100 G/3½ oz SPINACH

Calories	23
Protein	2.9 g
Fat	0.4 g
Carbohydrate	3.6 g
Fibre	2.2 g
Folate	194 mcg
Vitamin C	28 mg
Vitamin E	2 mg
Vitamin K	482 mcg
Iron	2.7 mg
Magnesium	79 mg
Potassium	558 mg
Lutein/Zeaxanthin	12,198 mcg
Beta-carotene	5626 mcg

Spiced chickpea and spinach soup

SERVES 4

1 tbsp vegetable oil
1 onion, finely chopped
2 garlic cloves, crushed
1 tsp cumin seeds
2 tsp medium curry powder
1 tsp hot chilli powder
*400 g/14 oz canned chickpeas,
    drained and rinsed*
*400 g/14 oz canned chopped
    tomatoes*
*500 ml/17 fl oz gluten-free
    vegetable stock*
*100 g/3½ oz spinach, de-stalked
    and chopped*
salt and pepper

Mint dressing
100 g/3½ oz natural yogurt
*2 tbsp finely chopped fresh mint
    leaves*
salt and pepper

Method

1 Heat the oil in a saucepan over a medium heat. Add the onion and sauté for 4–5 minutes, or until starting to soften.

2 Add the garlic, cumin seeds, curry and chilli powders and cook for 1 minute, stirring constantly.

3 Add the chickpeas, tomatoes and stock and season to taste with salt and pepper. Bring to the boil, then reduce the heat, cover and simmer for 15 minutes.

4 Meanwhile, to make the mint dressing, mix the yogurt and mint together with salt and pepper to taste. Cover and chill until ready to serve.

5 Stir the spinach into the soup and cook for a further 1–2 minutes, or until the spinach has wilted. Serve with a little of the mint dressing drizzled over.

78 MUSHROOMS

Mushrooms contain several health-boosting compounds which support the immune system and help prevent cancers and arthritis.

Some compounds found in mushrooms are known to help prevent a range of diseases. Dark-gilled and exotic types such as shiitake, chestnut and porcini, particularly, contain higher levels of these plant chemicals than the paler varieties. Lentinan and canthaxanthin boost the immune system and can help to prevent cancers, auto-immune diseases such as arthritis and lupus, and infections such as colds and bronchitis. Their high selenium content is also associated with protection from cancers. Mushrooms are also a useful source of protein for vegetarians and contain high levels of some of the B vitamins, including niacin, potassium to help reduce high blood pressure, and immune-boosting zinc.

- Contain compounds which can help prevent cancers and auto-immune diseases.
- Rich in the anti-cancer antioxidant mineral selenium.
- Good source of B vitamins including folate and niacin for nerves and energy production.
- Rich in potassium to help reduce high blood pressure.

Practical tips:
Store mushrooms in a paper bag in the refrigerator; don't store them in plastic. Wipe gently to clean if necessary and if practical, don't peel or remove the stalks as these contain high nutrient levels. Add mushrooms to casseroles, soups, stir-fries, pasta and rice dishes to increase the nutrient and protein content; stuff and bake larger mushrooms; or simply serve sliced mushrooms on toast.

DID YOU KNOW?

You should never pick mushrooms growing wild unless you get them checked for safety by a fungi expert. Several varieties (which can look harmless) are poisonous.

NUTRIENTS PER 100 G/3½ OZ CHESTNUT MUSHROOMS

Calories	22
Protein	2.5 g
Fat	Trace
Carbohydrate	4.3 g
Fibre	0.6 g
Folate	25 mcg
Niacin	3.8 mg
Calcium	18 mg
Potassium	448 mg
Selenium	26 mcg
Zinc	1.1 mg

Buckwheat, mushrooms and roasted squash

SERVES 4

1 kg/2 lb 4 oz squash, such as
    Crown Prince or Kabocha
1 tbsp thick balsamic vinegar
125 ml/4 fl oz olive oil
large knob of butter
225 g/8 oz roasted
    buckwheat, rinsed
1 egg, lightly beaten
450 ml/15 fl oz hot gluten-free
    vegetable stock
1 onion, halved and sliced
250 g/9 oz small chestnut
    mushrooms, quartered
2 tbsp lemon juice
6 tbsp chopped fresh
    flat-leaf parsley
25 g/1 oz walnut halves,
    roughly chopped
salt and pepper

Method

1 Preheat the oven to 200°C/400°F/Gas Mark 6. Cut the squash into eight wedges, peel and deseed.

2 Put the squash into a roasting tin and toss with the vinegar and 6 tablespoons of the oil. Season well with salt and pepper and dot with the butter. Roast in the preheated oven for 25–30 minutes, until slightly caramelized.

3 Meanwhile, put the buckwheat into a frying pan. Add the egg, stirring to coat the grains. Stir over a medium heat for 3 minutes, until the egg moisture has evaporated. Add the stock and ½ teaspoon of salt. Simmer for 9–10 minutes, until the grains are tender but not disintegrating. Remove from the heat and set aside.

4 Heat the remaining oil in the frying pan. Add the onion and fry over a medium heat for 10 minutes. Season to taste with salt and pepper. Add the mushrooms and fry for 5 minutes. Stir in the buckwheat, lemon juice and most of the parsley.

5 Transfer the buckwheat mixture to four plates and arrange the squash on top. Scatter over the walnuts and the remaining parsley. Serve immediately.

79 GARLIC

Garlic, used as a herb and medicine for thousands of years, is antibiotic and protective against digestive problems, heart disease and cancer.

Garlic, a member of the same allium family as onions, leeks and chives, is often used in small quantities but it can still make a great impact on health. It is rich in allicin, diallyl sulphide and ajoene – three sulphur compounds that are the main source of its health benefits. Research has found that garlic can help minimize the risk of both blood clots and arterial disease, and many types of cancer. It is also a powerful antibiotic, useful for helping battle infections in the intestine, and can also help cure fungal infections such as athlete's foot. It also appears to reduce the risk of stomach ulcers. Garlic is a useful source of the antioxidant vitamin C and also contains a little selenium, potassium and calcium.

- Regular consumption can help prevent heart disease.
- May significantly reduce the risk of colon, stomach and prostate cancers.
- Naturally antibiotic, antiviral and antifungal.
- Can help prevent stomach ulcers.

Practical tips:
Crush or chop fresh garlic and leave to stand for a few minutes before cooking to maximize the protective effects. Tests reveal that short cooking at low temperatures retains more beneficial compounds than longer, higher cooking. Chew fresh parsley after a garlic-rich meal to help avoid garlicky breath.

DID YOU KNOW?

Meat cooked at high temperatures, such as grilling or barbecuing, can be carcinogenic (cancer-promoting) but adding garlic, in a marinade for example, reduces the production of carcinogenic chemicals.

NUTRIENTS PER 2 FRESH MEDIUM-SIZED CLOVES

Calories	9
Protein	0.4 g
Fat	Trace
Carbohydrate	2 g
Fibre	Trace
Vitamin C	2 mg
Calcium	11 mg
Potassium	24 mg

Salmon and dill fishcakes with aïoli

MAKES 8

300 g/10½ oz cooked salmon,
   flaked

300 g/10½ oz mashed potato

8 tbsp chopped fresh dill, plus
   extra sprigs to garnish

6 spring onions, some green part
   included, finely chopped

1 tbsp coarsely grated lemon
   rind

1 tbsp cornflour, sifted

1 tsp salt

½ tsp pepper

2 eggs, lightly beaten

a little gluten-free plain flour,
   for dusting

vegetable oil, for frying

Aïoli

3 large garlic cloves, peeled

1 tsp sea salt flakes

2 egg yolks, at room temperature

250 ml/9 fl oz extra virgin olive oil

2 tbsp lemon juice

Method

1 In a large bowl, combine the salmon, potato, dill, spring onions and lemon rind, mixing lightly with a fork. Sprinkle with the cornflour, salt and pepper, then stir in the beaten egg. With floured hands, form into eight patties about 2 cm/¾ inch thick. Place on a baking paper-lined tray and chill for at least 2 hours.

2 To make the aïoli, crush the garlic cloves with the sea salt, using a mortar and pestle, to make a smooth paste. Transfer to a large bowl. Beat in the egg yolks. Add the oil, a few drops at a time, whisking constantly, until the mixture is thick and smooth. Beat in the lemon juice. Transfer to a serving bowl, cover with clingfilm and set aside.

3 Heat the oil in a frying pan and cook the fishcakes over a medium–high heat for 8 minutes, until golden. Turn and cook the other side for 4–5 minutes, until golden. Garnish with dill sprigs and serve immediately with the aïoli.

80 CHILLIES

Hot chillies are one of our favourite spices and can make a much larger contribution to your nutritional health than their size might indicate.

Chillies' main use in cooking – their heat – is also one of their main sources of health-giving properties. Capsaicin is what gives chillies this heat and this highly beneficial compound relieves the pain and inflammation associated with arthritis. It also appears to block the production of cancerous cells in cases of prostate cancer and acts as an anti-coagulant, thus helping protect against blood clots, heart attack or stroke. It can even ease nasal and lung congestion. Recent research shows that chilli consumption helps to lower the amount of insulin required to lower blood sugar after a meal and so could help diabetics and people who are insulin-resistant. This useful spice can also lower LDL cholesterol in the blood.

- Contain capsaicin to relieve pain and inflammation associated with arthritis.
- Strongly antioxidant to help beat prostate cancer and the diseases of ageing.
- Help lower LDL cholesterol.
- Rich in vitamin C and carotenes to boost the immune system.

Practical tips:
In general, the hotter the chilli the more capsaicin it contains – the hottest varieties include Habanero, bird's eye and Scotch bonnet. Jalapeños are mid-heat while Hungarian hot wax are mild. Removing the seeds from fresh chillies before use makes them milder but also removes some of the antioxidants. Take care not to rub your eyes when preparing chillies!

DID YOU KNOW?

Native to Central and South America, chillies have been cultivated for over 7,000 years – originally as a herbal medicine. After eating chillies the body's metabolic rate rises meaning you burn more calories.

NUTRIENTS PER MEDIUM-SIZED HOT RED CHILLI

Calories	12
Protein	0.5 g
Fat	Trace
Carbohydrate	2.6 g
Fibre	0.4 g
Niacin	0.4 mg
Vitamin C	43 mg
Iron	0.3 mg
Potassium	97 mg
Lutein/Zeaxanthin	213 mcg
Beta-carotene	160 mcg

Thai tofu cakes with chilli dip

SERVES 4

*300 g/10½ oz firm tofu, drained
    weight, coarsely grated*
*1 lemon grass stalk, finely
    chopped*
2 garlic cloves, chopped
*2.5-cm/1-inch piece fresh ginger,
    peeled and grated*
*2 kaffir lime leaves, finely
    chopped (optional)*
2 shallots, finely chopped
*2 fresh red chillies, deseeded
    and finely chopped*
4 tbsp chopped fresh coriander
*90 g/3¼ oz gluten-free plain
    flour, plus extra for dusting*
½ tsp salt
vegetable oil, for shallow-frying

Chilli dip
3 tbsp white distilled vinegar
2 spring onions, finely sliced
1 tbsp caster sugar
*2 fresh red chillies, deseeded
    and chopped*
2 tbsp chopped fresh coriander
pinch of salt

Method

1 To make the chilli dip, mix all the ingredients together in a small serving bowl and set aside.

2 Mix the tofu with the lemon grass, garlic, ginger, lime leaves (if using), shallots, chillies and coriander in a mixing bowl. Stir in the flour and salt to make a coarse, sticky paste. Cover and chill in the refrigerator for 1 hour to let the mixture firm up slightly.

3 Form the mixture into eight large, walnut-sized balls and, using floured hands, flatten into circles. Heat enough oil to cover the bottom of a large, heavy-based frying pan over a medium heat. Cook the tofu cakes in two batches, turning halfway through, for 4–6 minutes, or until golden brown. Drain on kitchen paper and serve warm with the chilli dip.

81 GINGER

While ginger is a favourite cooking spice, its unique plant compounds are also powerful against inflammation and digestive upsets, making it particularly useful for people recently diagnosed with gluten intolerance.

The most well-researched compounds in ginger are the gingerols, which give it much of its flavour and aroma. These can actually destroy colon, rectal and ovarian cancer cells. Gingerols also have a powerful anti-inflammatory action and improve pain, swelling and mobility in up to 75% of arthritis sufferers. Ginger has long been used as a remedy for nausea, morning sickness and seasickness and is also an aid to digestion, relaxing the intestines and helping to eliminate wind. Also present are terpenes, compounds that help keep the blood vessels dilated and can help lower blood pressure and prevent blood clots. Ginger may also ease migraines.

- Proven relief from the pain of arthritis.
- Strong anti-cancer action.
- Helps keep blood vessels healthy.
- Digestive aid.

Practical tips:
Fresh ginger contains the highest levels of beneficial compounds. Store in the refrigerator and peel and chop or grate as required. Ginger marries well with pears and rhubarb for a fruit compote or add to curries, stews, stir-fries and soups. Or make ginger tea – steep 1 heaped teaspoon grated ginger in hot water for 5 minutes.

DID YOU KNOW?

Ginger is a rhizome – a type of root – used medicinally and as a spice for at least 5,000 years across Asia before arriving in Europe around 2,000 years ago.

NUTRIENTS PER TABLESPOON FRESH CHOPPED GINGER

Calories	19
Protein	0.5 g
Fat	0.3 g
Carbohydrate	3.8 g
Fibre	0.7 g
Iron	0.6 mg
Magnesium	10 mg
Potassium	73 mg

Gingered carrot and pomegranate salad

SERVES 4

350 g/12 oz carrots,
finely grated
5-cm/2-inch piece of fresh
ginger, peeled and
finely grated
1 small pomegranate,
quartered
50 g/1¾ oz ready-to-eat
sprouting seeds, such as
alfalfa and radish sprouts

Dressing

3 tbsp light olive oil
3 tsp red wine vinegar
3 tsp pomegranate molasses
salt and pepper

Method

1 Put the carrots and ginger in a salad bowl. Flex the pomegranate pieces to pop out the seeds, prising any stubborn ones out with the tip of a small knife, and add to the bowl.

2 To make the dressing, put the oil, vinegar and pomegranate molasses in a clean jam jar, season with salt and pepper, screw on the lid and shake well. Drizzle over the salad and toss gently together. Cover and leave to marinate in the refrigerator for 30 minutes.

3 Sprinkle the sprouting seeds over the salad and serve.

Meat, fish and dairy

Each delicious food in this chapter has something special to offer for nutrition and health. Lean meats, such as beef and venison, are packed with high-quality protein and B vitamins, which can be in shortfall on a gluten-free diet, and high levels of iron for energy. Oily fish are rich in those hard-to-get omega-3 fats for heart health, while shellfish boast plenty of immune-boosting zinc. Cheese is one of our best sources of calcium, while yogurt is ideal for a sensitive gut, and eggs are rich in almost every vitamin and mineral you can name.

(C) High in carbohydrate

(F) Very good source of fibre

(V) Rich in vitamins and minerals

(D) Particularly good for digestive health

(P) High in protein

(N) Nutrient boost for gluten-free diet

82 CHICKEN

Lean chicken meat is one of the best protein choices you can make as it provides an impressive range of nutrients and compounds to boost your health.

Both chicken breast and leg meat are nutrient rich but while the breast is lower in fat and saturates, the darker leg meat is higher in iron and zinc. Chicken is very high in niacin (vitamin B3) and choline, another B vitamin – both of these help to lower LDL cholesterol and homocysteine in the blood, providing protection against cardiovascular disease. Chicken is high in the antioxidant mineral selenium, shown to help protect us from cancer, and is a very good source of iron which helps transport oxygen around the body. It is also rich in zinc, a powerful immune-booster. Chicken soup really is good for you – it contains a compound called carnosine, which helps to fight colds and flu, and cystine, an antibiotic.

- Rich in B vitamins to protect the heart and circulation.
- Excellent source of zinc, an immune-boosting mineral.
- Proved to contain natural antibiotic and immune-boosting compounds.

Practical tips:
Try to buy organic meat, which contains more omega-3 fats and vitamin E. When preparing raw chicken wash hands and utensils thoroughly afterwards and use a dedicated chopping board. Use the chicken carcass for soups, stocks and stews as the bones have the greatest immune-boosting effect. Make sure chicken is thoroughly cooked with no pink flesh.

DID YOU KNOW?

Chicken livers are very rich in iron and vitamin B12, both of which can be lacking in a gluten-free diet.

NUTRIENTS PER 100 G/3½ OZ LEAN CHICKEN BREAST (SKIN REMOVED)

Calories	114
Protein	21 g
Fat	2.6 g
Vitamin B6	0.7 mg
Vitamin B12	0.2 mcg
Choline	73 mg
Niacin	10.4 mg
Calcium	5 mg
Iron	0.5 mg
Magnesium	26 mg
Phosphorous	210 mg
Potassium	370 mg
Selenium	32 mcg
Zinc	0.6 mg

Chicken tacos

SERVES 4

1 ripe avocado
150 ml/5 fl oz natural yogurt
2 tbsp medium cornmeal
1 tsp chilli powder
½ tsp dried thyme
600 g/1 lb 5 oz skinless chicken
* breasts, cut into thin strips*
2 tbsp sunflower oil
1 red onion, sliced
1 large red pepper, deseeded
* and sliced*
1 large green pepper, deseeded
* and sliced*
8 gluten-free taco shells
salt and pepper
smoked paprika, to garnish

Method

1 Halve the avocado, remove the stone and scoop out the flesh, then purée in a blender with the yogurt. Season to taste with salt and pepper.
2 Mix together the cornmeal, chilli and thyme with salt and pepper to taste in a large bowl. Add the chicken and toss to coat evenly.
3 Heat the oil in a wok or large frying pan and stir-fry the onion and peppers for 3–4 minutes to soften. Remove and keep hot.
4 Add the chicken and stir-fry for 5–6 minutes, until evenly browned. Return the vegetables to the pan and stir-fry for a further 1–2 minutes.
5 Spoon the chicken mixture into the taco shells and top with a spoonful of the avocado mixture. Sprinkle with smoked paprika and serve.

83 TURKEY

Turkey is becoming more popular to eat year-round and its excellent health credentials make this versatile meat a very sensible choice in a gluten-free diet.

Turkey breast contains less fat than any other meat and its very high protein content means it is ideal for those watching their weight and for diabetics, as tests show it is a type of protein that can regulate insulin production. Turkey is surprisingly rich in vitamins and minerals. The light meat, the most popular type eaten by far, is a very good source of vitamin B6 and iron, while the dark meat is an even better source of most of the minerals. For example, lean turkey leg meat has a whopping 3.2 mg per 100 g of zinc – nearly half your RDA in a couple of slices. High in both potassium and phosphorous, turkey is an ideal food for helping to reduce high blood pressure and maintaining healthy bones and teeth.

- Very low in fat and high in nutrient-rich protein which helps to regulate insulin.
- Very good source of many of the B vitamins, particularly B6.
- Turkey leg meat is a good source of immune-boosting zinc.
- Phosphorous content helps maintain bones and teeth.

Practical tips:
Turkey can be used in almost any recipe where you would use chicken or pork. Minced leg meat makes a very good substitute for beef in burgers or a Bolognese sauce. If cooking a whole turkey, cook any stuffing separately to ensure that it and the bird are cooked properly all the way through.

DID YOU KNOW?

Meat from turkeys that graze on natural pasture contains a little more fat, including some omega-3 fats, and more carotenes than meat from penned turkeys.

NUTRIENTS PER 100 G/3½ OZ TURKEY BREAST (SKIN REMOVED)

Calories	115
Protein	23.5 g
Fat	1.6 g
Vitamin B5	0.7 mg
Vitamin B6	0.6 mg
Vitamin B12	0.5 mcg
Niacin	5.8 mg
Vitamin D	0.3 mcg
Iron	1.2 mg
Magnesium	27 mg
Phosphorous	204 mg
Potassium	305 mg
Selenium	24.5 mcg
Zinc	1.6 mg

Turkey, rice and cranberry salad

SERVES 4

150 g/5½ oz brown basmati rice
40 g/1½ oz wild rice
250 g/9 oz turkey breast
*   escalopes*
40 g/1½ oz dried cranberries
3 spring onions, finely chopped
200 g/7 oz tomatoes, diced
1 small red pepper, halved,
*   deseeded and cut into chunks*
55 g/2 oz rocket
40 g/1½ oz gluten-free, wafer-
*   thin sliced, cooked ham,*
*   cut into strips*
salt and pepper

Dressing

1½ tbsp cranberry sauce
1½ tbsp sherry vinegar
finely grated rind and juice
*   of 1 small lemon*
1 tsp gluten-free Dijon mustard
salt and pepper

Method

1 Put cold water in the base of a steamer, bring to the boil, then add the brown rice and wild rice and bring back to the boil. Put the turkey in the top of the steamer in a single layer, season with salt and pepper, then put it on the steamer base, cover and steam for 15 minutes, or until the turkey is cooked; cut into the middle of a slice to check that the meat is no longer pink and that the juices are clear and piping hot. Remove the steamer top and cook the rice for 5–10 minutes more, or until tender.

2 Dice the turkey and put it in a bowl. Add the cranberries. Drain and rinse the rice, then add to the bowl.

3 To make the dressing, put the cranberry sauce in a small saucepan and place over a low heat until just melted. Remove from the heat, then add the vinegar, lemon rind and juice, mustard and a little salt and pepper. Whisk together until smooth, then drizzle over the salad and leave to cool.

4 Add the spring onions, tomatoes and red pepper to the salad. Toss gently together, then divide between four plates. Top with the rocket and ham and serve.

84

DUCK

Duck has amazingly diverse and high levels of vitamins and minerals and is an extremely healthy meat, rich in high-quality complete protein.

Duck with its skin and fat left on contains around 28% fat, but over half of this is the healthy, unsaturated type. And fat-trimmed, the bird is, in fact, a relatively lean, high-protein meat at around only 6 g fat per 100 g. It is an especially rich source of selenium and zinc – important antioxidant minerals that protect against disease and the signs of ageing. Selenium has anti-cancer and thyroid-boosting properties, while zinc is a strong immune-booster. Duck is very rich in B vitamins, which support the nervous system and help keep your heart healthy. The B vitamin choline is powerfully anti-inflammatory and can also help minimize the symptoms of arthritis.

- Contains vitamins and antioxidants for heart protection.
- Very rich in a range of important minerals.
- High in the vitamin B group including anti-inflammatory choline.
- High in potassium to regulate blood pressure.

Practical tips:

Wild duck has an even higher proportion of mono- and polyunsaturated fats (around two-thirds) than farmed duck and is a leaner bird altogether. Duck goes particularly well with peas, beans, broccoli, oranges, apples and cherries. Anyone suffering from an illness, the elderly, infants and pregnant women should avoid eating under-cooked (pink) duck meat. Pierce the thickest part of the meat to check that the juices are clear and no longer pink.

DID YOU KNOW?

Perhaps the most famous dish we know from China is Peking duck, a specially bred small duck which is marinated in spices and then roasted – the skin is the most prized part of this dish.

NUTRIENTS PER 100 G/3½ OZ DUCK (SKIN REMOVED)

Calories	135
Protein	18.2 g
Fat	6 g
Vitamin A	29 mcg
Vitamin B1	0.4 mg
Vitamin B2	0.5 mg
Vitamin B5	1.6 mg
Vitamin B6	0.3 mg
Vitamin B12	0.4 mcg
Choline	53.6 mg
Folate	25 mcg
Niacin	5.3 mg
Iron	2.4 mg
Magnesium	19 mg
Potassium	271 mg
Selenium	13.9 mcg
Zinc	1.9 mg

Duck breasts with plum sauce

SERVES 4

1 tbsp duck fat or sunflower oil
4 duck breasts, about 350 g/
  12 oz each, finely scored
    through the skin to the fat
cooked French beans, to serve

Plum sauce

1 tbsp sunflower oil
1 shallot, finely chopped
1½ tbsp soft light brown sugar,
  plus extra, if needed
½ tsp ground ginger
4 plums, stoned and roughly
  chopped
4 tbsp gluten-free dry white wine
1 tsp orange juice, plus extra,
  if needed
salt and pepper

Method

1 Preheat the oven to 200°C/400°F/Gas Mark 6. To make the sauce, heat the oil in a frying pan over a high heat. Add the shallot and cook until soft. Stir in the sugar and ginger, add the plums and season to taste with salt and pepper. Stir until the sugar is dissolved and is just beginning to caramelize. Immediately add the wine and orange juice and bring to the boil, stirring. Reduce the heat to low and leave to simmer until the plums are tender and beginning to fall apart and the liquid is reduced. Taste and adjust the seasoning with salt and pepper, if needed. Add extra sugar or orange juice depending on how tart or sweet the plums are. Cover the sauce and set aside until required.

2 Meanwhile, melt the duck fat or oil in a large flameproof casserole wide enough to hold all the breasts in a single layer, or use a large frying pan with an ovenproof handle. Add the duck breasts, skin-side down, and fry for 3–5 minutes, or until golden brown. Turn the duck breasts skin-side up and put them in the oven for 10 minutes for medium-rare and up to 15 minutes for well done. Transfer the duck breasts to a chopping board, cover and leave to rest for 5 minutes.

3 Thinly slice the duck breasts diagonally and transfer to warmed plates. Add any accumulated juices to the sauce and quickly return the sauce to the boil to reheat. Serve immediately, with the sauce spooned over the duck breasts and the French beans alongside.

85

PORK

Pork is a particularly nutrient-rich meat. It is full of first-class protein, zinc, phosphorus, selenium, potassium and almost all the B vitamins.

A 100-g/3½-oz serving of pork provides around two-thirds of your RDA for vitamin B1, the B vitamin necessary for converting carbohydrates into energy and essential for muscle growth and repair. Its high levels of vitamins B2 and niacin help to regulate energy release throughout the day. Pork is rich in two minerals that strengthen your bones – phosphorus and magnesium – and provides a quarter of your RDA for zinc to bolster your immune system and help promote healthy new cells throughout your body. The same serving size of pork will also give you more than half of your daily needs of the antioxidant mineral selenium.

- High in top-quality protein to build and maintain muscle bulk and strength.
- Very good source of a wide range of B vitamins.
- High in bone-building minerals.
- One of the best sources of zinc for a healthy immune system.

Practical tips:
Pork tenderloin or fillet is an ideal cut to buy as it is extremely lean and tender. All pork should be thoroughly cooked with no pink left when you serve. Minced pork can be substituted for beef or lamb in almost any recipe. This meat goes well with green and red cabbage, rosemary and apples.

DID YOU KNOW?

Nearly half the fat in lean pork is the healthy mono-unsaturated kind – like that in olive oil – while only a third is saturated.

NUTRIENTS PER 100 G/3½ oz LEAN PORK

Calories	143
Protein	21.5 g
Fat	5.6 g
Vitamin B1	1 mg
Vitamin B2	0.3 mg
Vitamin B5	0.8 mg
Vitamin B6	0.5 mg
Vitamin B12	0.6 mcg
Choline	75.6 mg
Niacin	4.9 mg
Vitamin D	0.5 mcg
Iron	0.8 mg
Magnesium	23 mg
Phosphorous	211 mg
Potassium	389 mg
Selenium	36 mcg
Zinc	1.8 mg

Roast pork with gingered apples

SERVES 4

2 garlic cloves, crushed
4 tbsp gluten-free red wine
2 tbsp soft brown sugar
1 tbsp gluten-free tamari
    (Japanese soy sauce)
1 tsp sesame oil
½ tsp ground cinnamon
¼ tsp ground cloves
1 star anise, broken into
    pieces
½ tsp pepper
350 g/12 oz pork fillet
cooked French beans,
    to serve

Gingered apples

4 cooking apples, roughly
    chopped
1 tbsp rice vinegar
1 tbsp soft brown sugar
 4 tbsp apple juice
1 tbsp finely chopped fresh
    ginger

Method

1 In a large bowl combine the garlic, wine, brown sugar, tamari, sesame oil, cinnamon, cloves, star anise and pepper. Add the pork and toss to coat. Cover and refrigerate overnight.

2 Preheat the oven to 190°C/375°F/Gas Mark 5. Heat a non-stick frying pan over a high heat. Remove the pork from the marinade and sear in the hot pan. Cook for about 8 minutes, or until browned on all sides. Transfer the pork to an ovenproof dish and drizzle with half the marinade. Roast in the preheated oven for 15 minutes. Turn the meat, drizzle the remaining marinade over the top and roast for 30 minutes more, or until cooked through (insert a skewer into the centre of the meat and check that there is no pink meat).

3 Meanwhile, make the gingered apples. In a saucepan, combine all the ingredients and cook over a medium–high heat, until the liquid begins to boil. Reduce the heat to medium–low and simmer, stirring occasionally, for about 20 minutes, or until the apples are soft.

4 Remove the pork from the oven and set aside to rest for 5 minutes. Slice the meat and serve with the apples and French beans.

86 BEEF

Lean beef contains top-quality protein and is a vitamin B-rich, energy-giving, low-fat food perfect for a gluten-free diet.

Few people realise that lean beef is one of the lower-fat, lower-saturates meats with a very high protein percentage, and as such is a very useful food for a healthy balanced diet. It is one of the best sources of B vitamins, which have a variety of roles to play within your body. B vitamins are among the most important vitamins for the nervous system and in converting the food you eat into energy. They also provide cardiovascular protection. Beef contains valuable levels of many minerals and is a particularly good source of easily absorbed iron to prevent anaemia and fatigue. In addition, an average 125-g/4½-oz portion provides nearly half of your RDA of the immunity-boosting zinc.

- Low-fat and rich in high-quality complete protein.
- Rich in B vitamins.
- High in iron for healthy blood and protection against fatigue.
- Great source of zinc.

Practical tips:
The less expensive cuts of beef, such as shin, are the best cuts for dishes like casseroles and stews – simply cook the day before, refrigerate, then remove any solidified fat from the top before re-heating. Top cuts, such as fillet and rump, need to be cooked minimally to retain the vitamin B-rich juices. Make beef go further by using in soups and recipes, such as chilli con carne, with pulses and gluten-free grains.

DID YOU KNOW?

Pasture-raised beef, from animals that have eaten mostly grass and herbs, will offer extra nutritional benefit and contain high levels of omega-3 fats, vitamin E and carotenes.

NUTRIENTS PER 100 G/3½ OZ LEAN BEEF

Calories	117
Protein	23 g
Fat	2.7 g
Vitamin B6	1.3 mg
Vitamin B12	9 mcg
Choline	65 mg
Niacin	6.7 mg
Calcium	0.6 mg
Iron	1.8 mg
Magnesium	23 mg
Phosphorous	212 mg
Potassium	342 mg
Selenium	21 mcg
Zinc	3.6 mg

Steak and chips with watercress butter

SERVES 4

*1 bunch of watercress, plus
extra to garnish*
*85 g/3 oz unsalted butter,
softened*
*4 sirloin steaks, about
225 g/8 oz each*
4 tsp hot pepper sauce
salt and pepper

Chips

450 g/1 lb potatoes, peeled
2 tbsp sunflower oil

Method

1 To make the chips, preheat the oven to 200°C/400°F/Gas Mark 6. Cut the potatoes into thick, even-sized chips. Rinse them under cold running water and then dry well on a clean tea towel. Place in a bowl, add the oil and toss together until coated.

2 Spread the chips in a single layer on a baking sheet and cook in the preheated oven for 40–45 minutes, turning once, or until golden.

3 Using a sharp knife, finely chop enough watercress to fill 4 tablespoons. Place the butter in a small bowl and beat in the chopped watercress with a fork until fully incorporated. Cover with clingfilm and leave to chill in the refrigerator until required.

4 Preheat a griddle pan to high. Sprinkle each steak with 1 teaspoon of the hot pepper sauce, rubbing it in well. Season to taste with salt and pepper.

5 Cook the steaks on the preheated griddle for 2½ minutes each side for rare, 4 minutes each side for medium and 6 minutes each side for well done. Transfer to serving plates and serve immediately, topped with the watercress butter and accompanied by the chips. Garnish with watercress.

87 VENISON

Becoming more popular than ever, tender and lean venison meat is packed with iron, zinc and several other important nutrients vital for a gluten-free diet.

Extremely high in protein and lower in fat than most meats, game or poultry, venison is gaining in popularity as an alternative to beef as it has a similar richness of flavour and appearance. It is higher in iron than any other meat and is even richer in zinc than turkey leg meat. It also contains a whole day's recommended amount of vitamin B12 in a 100-g/3½-oz portion – this vitamin is only present in animal foods, not in vegetables, fruits or grains. Venison is also extremely high in niacin, which is needed for healthy skin and for the body to convert food to energy. Both B12 and niacin are likely to be in shortfall on a gluten-free diet.

- Very high in top-quality protein which can help the body regulate insulin levels.
- Low in fat.
- Very rich in iron for healthy blood and oxygen transportation.
- Contains large amounts of most of the B vitamins, particularly vitamin B12.

Practical tips:
Venison steaks are quick to cook and can be cooked in exactly the same way as beef steaks – brush the sides of the meat with oil then grill or fry in a dry pan. Cubed venison is ideal for casseroles and the meat goes particularly well with mushrooms, tomatoes, celery and chestnuts. Venison freezes very well.

DID YOU KNOW?

Venison contains a special type of fat called conjugated linoleic acid (CLA) which is thought to protect us against heart disease and some cancers, including colon cancer, and help to control body weight.

NUTRIENTS PER 100 G/3½ oz VENISON

Calories	149
Protein	30 g
Fat	2.4 g
Vitamin B1	0.3 mg
Vitamin B2	0.6 mg
Vitamin B5	0.9 mg
Vitamin B6	0.6 mg
Vitamin B12	3.6 mcg
Niacin	8.8 mg
Vitamin E	0.6 mg
Iron	4.2 mg
Magnesium	33 mg
Phosphorous	299 mg
Potassium	434 mg
Selenium	11 mcg
Zinc	4 mg

Chargrilled venison steaks

SERVES 4

4 venison steaks
fresh thyme sprigs, to garnish

Marinade

150 ml/5 fl oz gluten-free red
* wine*
2 tbsp olive oil
1 tbsp red wine vinegar
1 onion, chopped
1 tbsp chopped fresh parsley
1 tbsp chopped fresh thyme
1 bay leaf
1 tsp good-quality honey
½ tsp mild gluten-free mustard
salt and pepper

Method

1 Place the venison steaks in a shallow, non-metallic dish.
2 To make the marinade, combine the wine, oil, wine vinegar, onion, parsley, thyme, bay leaf, honey and mustard, and salt and pepper to taste, in a clean jam jar. Shake vigorously until well combined. Alternatively, using a fork, whisk the ingredients together in a bowl.
3 Pour the marinade mixture over the venison, cover and leave to marinate in the refrigerator overnight. Turn the steaks over in the mixture occasionally so that the meat is well coated.
4 Preheat the grill to high. Cook the venison under the hot grill for 2 minutes on each side to seal the meat.
5 Turn down the grill to medium, and cook for a further 4–10 minutes on each side, according to taste. Test the meat by inserting the tip of a knife into the meat – the juices will range from red when the meat is still rare to clear as the meat becomes well cooked.
6 Transfer the steaks to serving plates, garnish with fresh thyme sprigs and serve.

88 CRAB

Crab is a low-fat, high-protein shellfish containing l-tyrosine for a brainpower boost and high levels of several protective minerals, including selenium and zinc.

A 100-g/3½-oz portion of crab provides over half a day's recommended selenium intake for an adult. This is a powerful antioxidant mineral with anti-cancer action. In addition, a similar portion of crab gives you around half your day's RDA for zinc, a mineral that is not only antioxidant but also boosts the immune system and is vital for reproduction, growth and development. The body produces the amino acid l-tyrosine, but this is a natural food source of the protein that plays an important role in brain function. Crab is also a very good source of iron, calcium and potassium. And the meat is high in folate – a B vitamin that protects against birth defects and is vital for pregnant women. It is also linked to reducing the level of homocysteine in the blood, high levels of which are linked to heart disease.

- High in selenium to protect against cancer.
- Great source of zinc and other minerals.
- Contributes folate and a range of other B vitamins.
- Low in fat and saturates but high in protein.

Practical tips:
Try to buy cooked fresh or frozen crabmeat as canned crab is often high in sodium. Crab, particularly the nutrient-rich brown flesh, is very rich, so serve with simple, fresh flavours such as lemon.

DID YOU KNOW?

Dressed crab is the name given to crabmeat that has been cooked and removed from the shell to make it easy to use with no further preparation.

NUTRIENTS PER 100 G/3½ oz DRESSED CRAB (BROWN AND WHITE MEAT)

Calories	128
Protein	19.5 g
Fat	5.5 g
Folate	20 mcg
Niacin	1.5 mg
Calcium	26 mg
Iron	2.5 mg
Magnesium	58 mg
Potassium	250 mg
Selenium	36 mcg
Zinc	5.5 mg

Crab fritters with avocado salsa

SERVES 4

*200 g/7 oz lightly cooked
    sweetcorn*
70 g/2½ oz gluten-free plain flour
2 eggs, beaten
*300 g/10½ oz white crabmeat,
    drained if canned*
*1 small bunch fresh flat-leaf
    parsley, chopped*
3–4 tbsp olive oil
salt and pepper
lime wedges, to garnish

Avocado salsa

*1 small red onion,
    finely chopped*
*1 red pepper, deseeded
    and diced*
*1 yellow pepper, deseeded
    and diced*
*1 avocado, peeled, stoned
    and diced*
*1 mango, peeled, stoned
    and diced*
4 tomatoes
*juice and finely grated rind
    of 2 limes*
*1 large bunch fresh coriander,
    chopped*
salt and pepper

Method

1 To make the avocado salsa, put the onion, peppers, avocado
   and mango in a bowl. Chop the tomatoes into 1-cm/½-inch dice
   and add to the other ingredients. Stir in the lime juice and rind and
   coriander. Season to taste with salt and pepper.

2 Next make the fritters – put the sweetcorn, flour and eggs in a
   separate bowl and stir until well mixed. Lightly fold in the crabmeat
   and parsley, and season to taste with salt and pepper.

3 Heat the oil in a large frying pan over a medium–high heat. Drop
   spoonfuls of the crab fritter mixture into the hot oil and cook in
   batches for 2–3 minutes on each side until crisp and golden.
   Remove and drain on kitchen paper. Serve immediately with the
   avocado salsa and the lime wedges for squeezing over.

89 MUSSELS

Mussels contain a wide range of health-giving minerals and vitamins and, despite being low in fat, are a good source of essential fatty acids EPA and DHA.

Mussels are low in saturated fat and high in protein, and also contain some omega-3 essential fats which are strongly linked with heart and joint health. Unlike some other shellfish, such as prawns, they are low in cholesterol. They also provide a wide range of vitamins and many minerals in excellent amounts. A 150-g/5½-oz portion of mussels (shelled) will provide around a third of a day's recommended intake of iron for an adult (for healthy blood) and around three-quarters of a day's selenium requirement (for protection against cancer). They are a very good source of B vitamins, providing over 100% of your RDA for vitamin B12 and a quarter for folate. Mussels are also a helpful source of iodine for healthy thyroid function.

- A low-calorie, low-fat source of complete protein.
- Contain useful amounts of omega-3 essential fats.
- Rich in iron, iodine, zinc and selenium.
- Good source of B vitamins.

Practical tips:

If you buy fresh, live mussels you must prepare and cook them carefully – discard any that don't close tight when tapped. Steam, as per your recipe, for 3–4 minutes, until all the shells are open and discard any that don't open within a few minutes. You can also buy ready-cooked mussels from the supermarket. Mussels go very well with garlic, parsley and white wine and can be added to fish stews, soups, paella and shellfish salads.

DID YOU KNOW?

Many of the mussels that we eat today are farmed. You can easily tell which is which as farmed mussels have smooth, shiny, blue-black shells – wild ones are a duller blue-grey with white marks.

NUTRIENTS PER 100 G/3½ OZ SHELLED MUSSELS

Calories	86
Protein	11.9 g
Fat	2.2 g
EPA	0.41 g
DHA	0.16 g
Vitamin B12	12 mcg
Folate	42 mcg
Vitamin C	8 mg
Vitamin E	0.55 mg
Calcium	26 mg
Iron	3.9 mg
Magnesium	34 mg
Potassium	320 mg
Selenium	44.8 mg
Zinc	1.6 mg

Mussels in white wine

SERVES 4

2 kg/4 lb 8 oz live mussels,
  scrubbed and debearded
300 ml/10 fl oz gluten-free dry
  white wine
6 shallots, finely chopped
1 bouquet garni sachet
pepper
fresh flat-leaf parsley sprigs,
  to garnish

Method

1 Discard any mussels with broken shells and any that refuse to close
  when tapped.

2 Pour the wine into a large heavy-based saucepan, add the shallots
  and bouquet garni and season to taste with pepper. Bring to the
  boil over a medium heat, add the mussels and cover tightly. Cook,
  shaking the saucepan occasionally, for 3–4 minutes, or until the
  mussels have opened. Remove and discard the bouquet garni and
  any mussels that remain closed.

3 Using a slotted spoon, divide the mussels among individual serving
  dishes. Tilt the saucepan to let any sand settle, then spoon the
  cooking liquid over the mussels. Garnish with parsley sprigs and
  serve immediately.

90 SCALLOPS

Scallops are a treat that is also very good for you – these shellfish boost your vitamin B12, which can be low if you're following a gluten-free diet, and magnesium and can protect your arteries and bone health.

Scallops are an excellent source of vitamin B12, needed by our bodies for several functions, including the deactivation of homocysteine, a chemical that can damage blood vessel walls, and for healthy blood cell and nerve formation. High homocysteine levels are also linked with osteoporosis and a recent study found that osteoporosis occurred more frequently among women whose vitamin B12 status was deficient. A high intake of vitamin B12 can also help protect against colon cancer. Scallops are a very good source of magnesium, a regular intake of which helps build bone, release energy, regulate nerves and keep the heart healthy. They are also rich in tryptophan, an amino acid that boosts production of serotonin in our brains, linked with improved mood and relaxation.

- Low in calories and fat.
- Rich in magnesium which has several roles to play in body maintenance.
- A very good source of vitamin B12 for a variety of health benefits.
- Good source of minerals including immune-boosting zinc and potassium for blood pressure regulation.

Practical tips:
Scallops need cooking for a few minutes only or they will become chewy. The sweet flavour of scallops goes well with chilli, coriander, garlic and parsley, as well as lentils, peas and bacon.

DID YOU KNOW?

Scallops are an animal, not a fish. They are molluscs, and the part that we eat is the muscle that helps the animal swim and to open and close its shell.

NUTRIENTS PER 100 G/3½ OZ SHELLED SCALLOPS

Calories	106
Protein	16.2 g
Fat	3 g
Vitamin B12	1.5 mcg
Folate	16 mcg
Calcium	24 mg
Magnesium	56 mg
Potassium	280 mg
Selenium	22 mcg
Zinc	0.95 mg

Scallops with pea purée

SERVES 4

500 g/1 lb 2 oz frozen peas
2 large handfuls fresh mint
   leaves, roughly chopped
150 g/5½ oz butter
12 fat scallops, roes attached, if
   possible, and removed from
   their shells
salt and pepper

Method

1 Bring a large saucepan of water to the boil, then add the peas. Bring back to the boil and simmer for 3 minutes. Drain the peas, then put them in a food processor or blender with the mint, 100 g/3½ oz of the butter and a large pinch of salt. Process to a smooth purée, adding a little hot water if the mixture needs loosening. Taste for seasoning, cover and keep warm.

2 Pat the scallops dry, then season them well with salt and pepper. Place a large frying pan over a high heat and add the remaining butter. When the butter starts to smoke, add the scallops and sear them for 1–2 minutes on each side. They should be brown and crisp on the outside but light and moist in the middle. Remove the pan from the heat.

3 Spread a spoonful of pea purée on each of four plates and place three scallops on top of each. Season and serve immediately.

91

SQUID

Rich in protein, yet low in calories and fat, and with an abundance of useful B vitamins and minerals that can be low in a gluten-free diet, squid is one of the most useful seafoods to include in your diet.

Containing the whole range of B vitamins with a particularly high concentration of vitamins B2, B3, B5 and B12, squid is also a very good source of several minerals, including the antioxidant selenium, the immune-boosters iron and zinc, and potassium which helps to regulate blood pressure. Squid is a useful source of calcium and magnesium – both help bone strength and regulate the heartbeat, and calcium is a relaxant, helping beat insomnia. Higher in protein than many other types of fish, squid is a useful food to include in your diet if you are watching your weight as it is so low in calories. Squid even contains a small but useful amount of the omega-3 fats EPA and DHA, important for heart health.

- High in B vitamins.
- Rich in many minerals including selenium, iron and zinc.
- Contains calcium and magnesium to aid bone and heart health.
- High-protein, low-fat and low-calorie.

Practical tips:
Once cleaned and cut into strips, squid is quick and easy to cook. Take care not to overcook as this toughens it. It can be served hot, for example as part of a fish soup or Spanish paella, or added to salads. Frozen squid retains the vitamins and minerals of fresh.

DID YOU KNOW?

When a squid is threatened in the wild it often releases an inky-looking substance that we call squid ink. This is used in Mediterranean cooking to add colour and flavour to some dishes. There is evidence emerging that the ink may help prevent some cancers.

NUTRIENTS PER 100 G/3½ OZ FRESH SQUID (EDIBLE PORTION)

Calories	92
Protein	16 g
Fat	1.4 g
Vitamin B2	0.4 mg
Vitamin B5	0.5 mg
Vitamin B12	1.3 mcg
Niacin	2.2 mg
Calcium	32 mg
Iron	0.7 mg
Magnesium	33 mg
Potassium	246 mg
Selenium	44.8 mcg
Zinc	1.5 mg

Calamari with prawns and broad beans

SERVES 4–6

2 tbsp olive oil

4 spring onions, thinly sliced

2 garlic cloves, finely chopped

500 g/1 lb 2 oz cleaned squid
    bodies, thickly sliced

100 ml/3½ fl oz gluten-free dry
    white wine

225 g/8 oz fresh or frozen baby
    broad beans

250 g/9 oz raw king prawns,
    peeled and deveined

4 tbsp chopped fresh flat-leaf
    parsley

salt and pepper

Method

1 Heat the oil in a large frying pan with a lid, add the spring onions and cook over a medium heat, stirring occasionally, for 4–5 minutes, until soft.

2 Add the garlic and cook, stirring, for 30 seconds, until soft.

3 Add the squid and cook over a high heat, stirring occasionally, for 2 minutes, or until golden brown.

4 Stir in the wine and bring to the boil. Add the beans, reduce the heat, cover and simmer for 5–8 minutes, if using fresh beans, or 4–5 minutes, if using frozen beans, until tender.

5 Add the prawns, re-cover and simmer for a further 2–3 minutes, until the prawns turn pink and start to curl.

6 Stir in the parsley and season to taste with salt and pepper. Serve immediately.

92 SEA BASS

While sea bass is classed as a white fish, it contains several nutrients more commonly associated with oily fish or shellfish and will boost your intake of nutrients sometimes lacking in a gluten-free diet.

Sea bass is one of the few fish classed in the 'white fish' category to contain useful amounts of the long-chain fats EPA and DHA, found only in fish (more usually in oily fish such as salmon). A third of sea bass's total fat content is these omega-3 fats, and one 100-g/3½-oz portion will give you more than a day's recommended intake to help prevent cardiovascular disease. The fish also boasts a long list of vitamins and minerals and is a particularly good source of most of the B vitamins, including vitamin B12, which we need on a daily basis as it is a water-soluble vitamin and not stored in the body. It also contains an impressive amount of the anti-cancer, antioxidant mineral selenium.

- Higher in omega-3 EPA and DHA fats than most other white fish.
- Good source of vitamins A, D and E and most of the B vitamins.
- Rich in a broad spectrum of minerals including phosphorous and magnesium for heart and bone health.
- Good source of selenium.

Practical tips:
Sea bass has a delicate yet distinctive flavour and a fine texture and is becoming one of the most popular fish to eat across the world. Whole fish can be baked or pan fried, fillets can be steamed, grilled or pan fried, and all cuts can be wrapped in greaseproof paper with flavourings and cooked *en papillote*. Eat or freeze on the day you buy it.

DID YOU KNOW?

Dicentrarchus labrax, the European sea bass, is the variety of bass eaten in the UK and it is one of the most widely eaten across Mediterranean countries. In Greece it is called *lavraki* – a word that also means a catch that is prized.

NUTRIENTS PER 100 G/3½ oz FRESH SEA BASS

Calories	97
Protein	18.4 g
Fat	2 g
EPA	0.2 g
DHA	0.4 g
Vitamin A	46 mcg
Vitamin B5	0.8 mg
Vitamin B6	0.4 mg
Vitamin B12	0.3 mcg
Choline	60.8 mg
Niacin	1.6 mg
Vitamin D	5.6 mcg
Vitamin E	0.8 mg
Magnesium	41 mg
Phosphorous	194 mg
Potassium	256 mg
Selenium	36 mcg
Zinc	0.4 mg

Baked sea bass with white bean purée

SERVES 4

2 tbsp olive oil
1 tbsp fresh thyme leaves
4 large sea bass fillets, about
  175 g/6 oz each
salt and pepper
cherry tomatoes, to serve

White bean purée

3 tbsp olive oil
2 garlic cloves, chopped
800 g/1 lb 12 oz canned
  cannellini or butter beans,
  drained and rinsed
juice of 1 lemon
2–3 tbsp water
4 tbsp chopped fresh flat-leaf
  parsley
salt and pepper

Method

1 Preheat the oven to 200°C/400°F/Gas Mark 6. Mix together the oil, thyme and salt and pepper to taste in a small bowl. Arrange the sea bass fillets on a baking tray, pour over the oil mixture and carefully turn to coat well. Put the tray on the top shelf of the preheated oven and bake for 15 minutes.

2 Meanwhile, make the white bean purée. Heat the oil in a saucepan over a medium heat, add the garlic and cook, stirring, for 1 minute. Add the beans and heat through for 3–4 minutes, then add the lemon juice and salt and pepper to taste. Transfer to a food processor or blender, add the water and process lightly until you have a purée. Alternatively, mash thoroughly with a fork. Stir the parsley into the purée.

3 Serve the sea bass fillets immediately, on top of the warm white bean purée with a drizzle of any pan juices and the cherry tomatoes.

93 SALMON

Salmon is an excellent source of the essential omega-3 fats and is rich in a range of B vitamins making it an ideal fish for a gluten-free diet.

Salmon is a major source of vital fish oils and its many health benefits include protection against arthritis, heart disease, blood clots, stroke, high blood pressure and high blood cholesterol. The EPA and DHA fatty acids it contains are linked with a reduced risk of depression and skin and breast cancer. They also help combat insulin resistance, which can be a precursor to diabetes, and help improve eczema and other inflammatory skin conditions. In addition, salmon contains a great range of the B vitamins – most of which are often in short supply on a gluten-free diet.

- Protection against cardiovascular diseases and stroke.
- Helps keep brain healthy and improves insulin resistance.
- Fish oils help keep skin smooth, can help beat eczema and help prevent dry eyes.
- Helps minimize joint pain and arthritis and may reduce the risk of some cancers.

Practical tips:
For optimum omega-3 content cook salmon lightly – poach or grill it. Frozen salmon retains the beneficial oils, vitamins and minerals, but canned salmon loses a proportion of these nutrients. Hot- and cold-smoked salmon retain a good proportion of the omega-3 fats but eat in moderation as the smoking process may increase the risk of cancer.

DID YOU KNOW?

Although salmon is often eaten raw in some parts of the world (in Japanese sushi, etc.) it may be best to avoid it unless it has been pre-frozen as it can contain parasites that cause food poisoning and other digestive problems.

NUTRIENTS PER 100 g/3½ oz FRESH SALMON FILLET

Calories	183
Protein	19.9 g
Fat	10.8 g
EPA	0.69 g
DHA	1.29 g
Vitamin B6	0.64 mg
Vitamin B12	2.8 mcg
Folate	26 mcg
Niacin	7.5 mg
Vitamin C	3.9 mg
Vitamin E	1.9 mg
Magnesium	28 mg
Potassium	362 mg
Selenium	36.5 mcg
Zinc	0.4 mg

Salmon fingers with potato wedges

SERVES 4

150 g/5½ oz fine cornmeal
1 tsp paprika
400 g/14 oz salmon fillet,
    skinned and sliced into
    12 chunky fingers
1 egg, beaten
sunflower oil, for frying

Potato wedges

500 g/1 lb 2 oz potatoes, cut
    into thick wedges
1–2 tbsp olive oil
½ tsp paprika
salt

Method

1 Preheat the oven to 200°C/400°F/Gas Mark 6. To make the wedges, dry the potato wedges on a clean tea towel. Spoon the oil into a roasting tin and put into the preheated oven briefly to heat. Add the potatoes to the tin and toss in the warm oil until well coated. Sprinkle with paprika and salt to taste and roast for 30 minutes, turning once, until crisp and golden.

2 Meanwhile, mix the cornmeal and paprika together on a plate. Dip each salmon finger into the beaten egg, then roll in the cornmeal mixture until evenly coated.

3 Heat enough oil to cover the base of a large, heavy-based frying pan over a medium heat. Carefully arrange half the salmon fingers in the pan and cook for 6 minutes, turning halfway through, until golden. Drain on kitchen paper and keep warm while you cook the remaining salmon fingers. Serve with the potato wedges.

94 TUNA

Another important source of heart-protecting omega-3 fats, fresh tuna is also rich in vitamin E, for healthy skin, and the B vitamins, especially B12, which are sometimes lacking in a gluten-free diet.

An excellent source of protein and especially rich in selenium and magnesium, a small 100-g/3½-oz portion of tuna also contains around 20% of your daily vitamin E needs. The fish has a good content of EPA and DHA. DHA is particularly effective in keeping our hearts healthy and may also improve brain function and minimize depression. Eating tuna on a regular basis cuts death from heart disease by up to 50% – just one small 100-g/3½-oz portion a week can provide the weekly recommended 1.4 g of these fats. Tuna is also a particularly good source of B vitamins, with more than twice your RDA of vitamin B12 (vital for healthy blood and nerves) and half your niacin (which helps release energy from food).

- The protective fats found in tuna can cut heart disease deaths by up to 50%.
- High in protein.
- Rich in antioxidants selenium and magnesium for heart health.
- Rich in vitamin B12 and the range of B vitamins.

Practical tips:
Fresh or frozen tuna with its dense, meaty, flavourful flesh is an ideal choice of fish for non-fish lovers and is quick to cook. To retain all the health benefits of the omega-3 fats cook for a short time only – cook a 2-cm/¾-inch thick steak in a pan brushed with oil for 1–1½ minutes on each side. Or try adding sliced tuna to a stir-fry with sliced vegetables.

DID YOU KNOW?

Canned tuna contains much less omega-3 fat than fresh or frozen tuna and isn't classed as an oily fish at all.

NUTRIENTS PER 100 G/3½ OZ FRESH TUNA FILLET

Calories	144
Protein	23 g
Fat	4.9 g
EPA	0.4 g
DHA	1.2 g
Vitamin B5	1 mg
Vitamin B6	0.5 mg
Vitamin B12	9.4 mcg
Niacin	8.3 mg
Vitamin E	1 mg
Iron	1 mg
Magnesium	50 mg
Potassium	252 mg
Selenium	36 mcg
Zinc	0.6 mg

Tuna steaks with Mediterranean butter

SERVES 4

4 tuna steaks, each about
 4 cm/1½ inches thick,
 at room temperature
olive oil, for brushing
salt and pepper
mixed salad leaves, to serve

Mediterranean butter

1 garlic clove, finely chopped
125 g/4½ oz butter, softened
2 tbsp chopped fresh dill
4 black olives in brine, drained,
 stoned and very finely
 chopped
2 anchovy fillets in oil, drained
 and very finely chopped
2 sun-dried tomatoes in oil,
 drained and very finely
 chopped
finely grated rind of 1 lemon
pinch of cayenne pepper,
 or to taste
salt and pepper

Method

1 At least 3 hours before you plan to cook the tuna, make the butter. Put the garlic clove on a chopping board and sprinkle with salt. Use the flat side of a knife to crush and scrape the garlic until a paste forms. Beat the garlic, butter, dill, olives, anchovies, sun-dried tomatoes, lemon rind and cayenne pepper together in a bowl until all the ingredients are mixed. Season to taste with salt and pepper.

2 Scrape the butter mixture onto a piece of greaseproof paper and roll into a short log about 2.5 cm/1 inch thick. Twist the ends of the paper to make a compact shape, then cut off any excess paper from one end. Stand the butter log upright in a glass and chill for at least 3 hours.

3 Heat a large griddle pan over a high heat. Brush the tuna with oil and season with salt and pepper on both sides. Place the tuna steaks in the pan and griddle for 2 minutes. Brush the tuna with a little more oil, turn the steaks over and continue cooking for 1 minute for medium-rare or up to 2½ minutes for well done. Transfer the tuna steaks to plates and top each with a slice of the chilled butter. Serve immediately with mixed salad leaves.

95 TROUT

Trout has many of the benefits of salmon but is a lighter fish with less fat and more protein. It provides an excellent range of essential vitamins and minerals for the gluten-free diet.

Trout is classed as an oily fish and makes a good alternative to salmon if you find that too rich. Although trout contains fewer omega-3 fats (though is still a good source of these) and some of the B vitamins than salmon, it more than makes up for this by containing more vitamin B12 and more calcium, iron, magnesium and zinc. Trout is extremely rich in potassium, a mineral that has several roles to play. It helps your heart beat properly and works with magnesium to help prevent an irregular heartbeat or palpitations. If you have high blood pressure, a weak heart or heart rhythm problems, getting enough potassium is especially important – and eating a potassium-rich diet may lower your cholesterol, too.

- Contains heart-friendly omega-3 fats.
- Very high in potassium for a healthy heart.
- Good range of B vitamins and minerals.
- Cholesterol-lowering.

Practical tips:
The delicate flesh of trout needs only light cooking – try baking or grilling and serve with lemon wedges and salad. Alternatively, try steaming whole fish with oriental flavours such as chilli, ginger, garlic and soy. Trout freezes very well – freeze when as fresh as possible.

DID YOU KNOW?

Trout is a common freshwater fish native to the UK, and is a member of the salmon family.

NUTRIENTS PER 100 G/3½ oz FRESH TROUT FILLET

Calories	119
Protein	20.5 g
Fat	3.5 g
EPA	0.17 g
DHA	0.42 g
Vitamin B6	0.4 mg
Vitamin B12	4.5 mcg
Niacin	5.4 mg
Calcium	67 mg
Iron	0.7 mg
Magnesium	31 mg
Potassium	481 mg
Selenium	13 mcg
Zinc	1 mg

Trout terrine

SERVES 4

225 g/8 oz trout fillets
175 g/6 oz smoked trout, finely sliced
150 g/5½ oz cream cheese
1 tbsp crème fraîche
1 tbsp horseradish sauce
grated rind of 1 lemon
2 tbsp chopped fresh flat-leaf parsley
1 tbsp snipped fresh chives
salt and pepper
salad leaves, to serve

Method

1 Poach the trout fillets in a little water in a frying pan for 3–4 minutes, or until cooked. Drain well and allow to cool.

2 Line a small loaf tin with clingfilm and then line with the slices of smoked trout, leaving enough to overlap the top.

3 Skin and flake the trout fillets and mix together with the cream cheese, crème fraîche, horseradish sauce and lemon rind, and season with salt and pepper to taste.

4 Spoon a layer of the trout mixture into the lined tin. Sprinkle over the herbs. Cover with the remaining trout mixture. Fold over the smoked trout edges and cover with clingfilm. Press down and chill in the refrigerator for 2–3 hours.

5 Turn out of the tin and slice carefully using a sharp knife. Serve immediately garnished with salad leaves.

96

CHEDDAR CHEESE

Hard cheeses, such as Cheddar, have much to offer within a healthy gluten-free diet as they pack in a high level of nutrients and are one of the foods richest in calcium.

Cheddar cheese is very rich in calcium – one 50-g/1¾-oz portion provides over a third of your RDA. This mineral, along with magnesium also found in cheese, is essential for building and maintaining bone density and strength. Cheese also contains phosphorous, which binds with calcium to form bones and teeth; vitamin D, vital for bone formation; and arginine which helps reduce tooth sensitivity. Calcium-rich foods speed up the metabolic rate, helping us to burn fat. The casein in cheese also helps boost metabolism, while the high protein and fat content keeps you feeling fuller for longer. Hard cheese is a good source of iodine, too, which helps the thyroid function, and vitamins B2, B12 and A, all of which may be in shortfall on a gluten-free diet.

- High calcium content for healthy bones.
- Rich in minerals and compounds to keep teeth healthy.
- Helps speed up the metabolic rate and burn fat.
- One of the few good non-meat sources of vitamin B12.

Practical tips:
Hard cheese keeps best wrapped in greaseproof paper and then stored in a container with airholes. It can also be frozen, whole or grated. Add cheese to your diet by sprinkling it on soups, casseroles and pasta dishes.

DID YOU KNOW?

It takes around 10 litres (over 2 gallons) of milk to make 1 kg/2 lb 4 oz of Cheddar. Mild Cheddar is about 3 months old whereas extra mature, or vintage, Cheddars are matured for around 18 months.

NUTRIENTS PER 50 G/1¾ oz CHEDDAR CHEESE

Calories	202
Protein	12.5 g
Fat	16.5 g
Vitamin A	150 mcg
Vitamin B2	0.2 mg
Vitamin B12	0.4 mcg
Vitamin D	0.3 mcg
Calcium	361 mg
Fluoride	17.9 mcg
Iodine	25 mcg
Magnesium	20 mg
Phosphorous	252 mg
Potassium	49 mg
Selenium	7 mcg
Zinc	1.5 mg

Courgette and cheese gratin

SERVES 4–6

*55 g/2 oz butter, plus extra for
    greasing*
6 courgettes, sliced
*2 tbsp chopped fresh tarragon
    or a mixture of fresh mint,
    tarragon and flat-leaf parsley*
*200 g/7 oz Cheddar cheese,
    grated*
125 ml/4 fl oz milk
125 ml/4 fl oz double cream
2 eggs, beaten
freshly grated nutmeg
salt and pepper

Method

1 Preheat the oven to 180°C/350°F/Gas Mark 4. Grease a large baking dish.

2 Melt the butter in a large frying pan over a medium-high heat. Add the courgettes and sauté for 4–6 minutes, turning the slices over occasionally, until coloured on both sides. Remove from the pan and drain on kitchen paper, then season to taste with salt and pepper.

3 Spread half the courgettes over the base of the prepared dish. Sprinkle with half of the herbs and 85 g/3 oz of the cheese. Repeat these layers once more.

4 Mix the milk, cream and eggs together in a jug and add nutmeg and salt and pepper to taste. Pour this liquid over the courgettes, then sprinkle the top with the remaining cheese.

5 Bake in the preheated oven for 35–45 minutes, or until it is set in the centre and golden brown. Remove from the oven and leave to stand for 5 minutes before serving straight from the dish.

97

GOAT'S CHEESE

Goat's cheese has an unusual composition for a dairy product, being high in probiotics and low in lactose, and is a great cheese for anyone with digestive problems.

Goat's milk cheese contains types of fatty acids that are similar to human milk and easier for the body to process than other milks. It is also easier to digest because the fat globules it contains are smaller than those in cow's milk. The cheese is rich in probiotics – bacteria that can help the digestion process and may ease mild stomach problems. Relatively low in lactose, goat's cheese is often suitable for people who are mildly lactose intolerant. A serving provides a similar vitamin and mineral content to hard cheeses and is a very good source of vitamin A, phosphorus, niacin and vitamin B1. It is also high in calcium which is not only vital for bone development and maintenance but also has a fat-burning effect for weight control.

- Fat types found in goat's cheese are easily digestible.
- Rich in probiotics for gut health.
- Good source of range of vitamins and minerals.
- High calcium content for bone health and weight control.

Practical tips:
Delicious eaten cold on gluten-free wholegrain biscuits or toast, goat's cheese is also great to use as a melted cheese topping in a variety of recipes. It goes very well with beetroot, onions, apples, celery and grapes.

DID YOU KNOW?

It takes around 5 litres (over 1 gallon) of milk to make 450 g/1 lb of goat's cheese and it is one of the earliest dairy foods known to have been produced.

NUTRIENTS PER 50 G/1¾ oz GOAT'S CHEESE

Calories	182
Protein	10.8 g
Fat	15 g
Vitamin A	220 mcg
Vitamin B2	0.3 mg
Vitamin B3	0.6 mg
Vitamin D	0.3 mcg
Calcium	149 mg
Magnesium	15 mg
Phosphorous	188 mg
Potassium	79 mg
Zinc	0.3 mg

Lentil and goat's cheese tomatoes

SERVES 4

55 g/2 oz dried Puy lentils
4 beef tomatoes
1 tbsp olive oil
2 large shallots, finely chopped
1 garlic clove, crushed
1 tbsp chopped fresh thyme
100 g/3½ oz hard goat's cheese,
    diced
salt and pepper
mixed salad, to serve

Method

1 Bring a small saucepan of water to the boil over a medium–high heat. Add the lentils, return to the boil and cook for 20–25 minutes, or until tender. Drain well.

2 Meanwhile, preheat the oven to 200°C/400°F/Gas Mark 6. Cut a slice from the tops of the tomatoes and set aside. Scoop out the pulp from the centre and chop roughly.

3 Heat the oil in a frying pan over a medium heat and fry the shallots, stirring, for 3–4 minutes to soften. Add the garlic and chopped tomato pulp and cook for a further 3–4 minutes, or until any excess liquid has evaporated.

4 Place the tomatoes in a shallow baking dish. Stir the lentils and thyme into the frying pan, and season to taste with salt and pepper. Stir in the goat's cheese and then spoon the mixture into the tomatoes.

5 Place the lids on the tomatoes and bake in the preheated oven for 15–20 minutes, or until tender. Serve immediately with mixed salad.

98 EGGS

Eggs contain almost the whole range of nutrients that can be lacking on a gluten-free diet and have several additional health benefits.

Hens' eggs provide the whole range of essential amino acids that make up a complete protein and so are especially useful in a vegetarian diet. They are high in most of the major vitamins including A, B2, B12, D and E, and minerals including calcium, zinc and phosphorous. It can be hard to get adequate amounts of all these nutrients on a gluten-free diet. Eggs are particularly high in the B vitamin choline, which helps prevent high levels of harmful homocysteine (linked to cardiovascular disease and osteoporosis) in the blood. Eggs from hens allowed to eat a natural, pasture/woodland diet are a good source of heart-friendly omega-3 fats but even other types of eggs have been shown to raise 'good' HDL cholesterol.

- Excellent source of complete protein.
- High in many vitamins and minerals.
- Very high in choline for heart health.
- Can help raise HDL cholesterol.

Practical tips:
Store eggs in the refrigerator or at cool room temperature – allow to warm slightly in the kitchen before boiling in their shells or the shells may crack. If using several eggs in a recipe, break each one into a bowl separately first to check the egg looks fresh (rounded yolk, cloudy white, no odour).

DID YOU KNOW?

The World Health Organization uses eggs as its reference point for rating the quality of protein in all other foods. Raw and lightly cooked eggs should be avoided by young children, the elderly, pregnant women and ill or infirm people because of the risk of contamination from salmonella.

NUTRIENTS PER MEDIUM-SIZED EGG

Calories	80
Protein	7 g
Fat	5.3 g
Vitamin A	91 mcg
Vitamin B2	0.3 mg
Vitamin B12	0.5 mcg
Choline	141 mg
Folate	26 mcg
Vitamin D	11.5 mcg
Vitamin E	0.6 mg
Calcium	31 mg
Phosphorous	111 mg
Potassium	77 mg
Zinc	0.7 mg

Angel food cake

SERVES 8

butter, for greasing
10 egg whites
60 g/2¼ oz white rice flour
60 g/2¼ oz tapioca flour
60 g/2¼ oz cornflour
60 g/2¼ oz potato flour
300 g/10½ oz caster sugar
1½ tsp cream of tartar
½ tsp vanilla extract
½ tsp salt
icing sugar, for dusting

Method

1 Preheat the oven to 180°C/ 350°F/Gas Mark 4. Grease a 20-cm/8-inch round cake tin and line with baking paper.

2 Allow the egg whites to sit for approximately 30 minutes at room temperature in a large bowl. Sift the white rice flour, tapioca flour, cornflour, potato flour and 175 g/6 oz of the sugar into a separate bowl.

3 Whisk the egg whites together with the cream of tartar, vanilla extract and salt until soft peaks form. Gradually add the remaining sugar until stiff peaks develop. Add the flour mixture and fold in carefully to combine.

4 Spoon the mixture into the prepared tin and bake in the preheated oven for approximately 45 minutes, until firm to the touch and a skewer inserted in the centre comes out clean.

5 Remove from the oven and, leaving the cake in the tin, turn upside-down to cool on a wire rack. Once cool, remove from the tin and dust with icing sugar.

99

MILK

Rich in calcium and several other nutrients that a gluten-free diet can often lack, milk is worth including in your diet every day.

The amount of nutrients milk contains means it is really more of a food than a drink. A quarter of the calories in a typical serving of 200 ml/7 fl oz come from protein and around a third from fat – both help keep hunger pangs at bay, so milk is an ideal snack. This amount will also contain around a third of your RDA of calcium (which can be low on a gluten-free diet), all of your RDA of vitamin B12, and a quarter of your RDA of vitamin B2 – a vitamin that helps release the energy from both protein and fat in your body. Milk is a good source of choline (a lesser-known B vitamin that protects against cardiovascular disease, osteoporosis and arthritis) and vitamin A for healthy eyes and skin.

- Very good source of calcium to maintain and repair bones and to help prevent osteoporosis.
- Contains most of the B vitamins.
- High level of vitamin A.
- Choline content protects against heart disease and arthritis.

Practical tips:
Store milk in the refrigerator to retain its B vitamins and keep well-sealed so that it doesn't absorb aromas from other foods in the refrigerator. Make a healthy, potassium-rich milkshake by blending milk with a banana. A glass of milk before bedtime really can help you sleep as the tryptophan it contains will boost brain serotonin and aid relaxation.

DID YOU KNOW?

Organic and/or grass-fed cow's milk is a good source of omega-3 fats, as well as a variety of antioxidant compounds and vitamin E. The milk from penned animals fed on grain-based feed is not as rich in these nutrients.

NUTRIENTS PER 200 ml/7 fl oz SEMI-SKIMMED (2% FAT) MILK

Calories	100
Protein	6.6 g
Fat	4 g
Carbohydrate	9.6 g
Vitamin A	61.2 mcg
Vitamin B2	0.4 mg
Vitamin B5	0.7 mg
Vitamin B12	1 mcg
Choline	32.8 mg
Calcium	240 mg
Magnesium	22 mg
Potassium	280 mg
Zinc	1 mg

Crème caramel

SERVES 4

butter, for greasing
200 g/7 oz caster sugar
4 tbsp water
½ lemon
500 ml/17 fl oz milk
1 vanilla pod
2 large eggs
2 large egg yolks

Method

1 Preheat the oven to 160°C/325°F/Gas Mark 3. Lightly grease the base and sides of four ramekin dishes. To make the caramel, place 75 g/2¾ oz of the sugar with the water in a saucepan over a medium-high heat and cook, stirring, until the sugar dissolves. Boil until the syrup turns a deep golden-brown, then immediately remove from the heat and squeeze in a few drops of lemon juice. Divide evenly between the ramekin dishes, swirl around to line the base and set aside.

2 Pour the milk into a saucepan. Slit the vanilla pod lengthways and add it to the milk. Bring to the boil, remove the saucepan from the heat and stir in the remaining sugar, stirring until it dissolves. Keep to one side.

3 Beat the eggs and egg yolks together in a bowl. Pour the milk mixture over them, whisking. Remove the vanilla pod. Strain the egg mixture into a bowl, then divide evenly between the ramekin dishes.

4 Place the dishes in a roasting tin. Boil a kettle and carefully pour the hot water into the tin so that it comes two-thirds of the way up the sides of the dishes.

5 Bake in the preheated oven for 1–1¼ hours, or until a knife inserted in the centre comes out clean. Leave to cool completely. Cover with clingfilm and leave to chill for at least 24 hours.

6 Run a round-bladed knife around the edge of each dish. Place an up-turned serving plate, with a rim, on top of each dish, then invert the plate and dish, giving a sharp shake halfway over. Lift off the ramekin dishes and serve.

100 YOGURT

One of the healthiest dairy foods to include in a gluten-free diet, live or 'bio' natural yogurt has a special role in maintaining gut health.

Yogurt has long been eaten for its health-giving properties. Live yogurt, which contains billions of bacteria, such as acidophilus and bifidobacteria, is a valuable digestive aid. These 'friendly' bacteria line the gut, protect the digestive system from harm, help to relieve bloating and constipation and boost the immune system. Yogurt also has many of the health benefits of cheese, being high in calcium for bone health and aiding relaxation and sleep. For those watching their weight, yogurt can even boost fat loss, particularly around the waist. Live yogurt may also lower LDL cholesterol and raise HDL.

• Helps keep the digestive system healthy and regular.
• Boosts the immune system.
• High calcium content for bone health and relaxation.
• Burns abdominal fat and improves blood cholesterol profile.

Practical tips:
Yogurt can be made with cow's, goat's, sheep's or buffalo's milk, but cow's milk yogurt is the most common. Yogurt, fruit and wholegrain cereal is one of the healthiest breakfasts you can eat. Also try stirring natural yogurt into soups, curries and sauces, or use as a topping for dessert instead of cream. Bring to room temperature before adding to hot dishes to avoid the yogurt curdling.

DID YOU KNOW?

Yogurt got its name from the Turkish word *yogurur*, which means 'long life', and has been consumed throughout Turkey and the Middle East for over 5,000 years.

NUTRIENTS PER 100 G/3½ OZ LIVE WHOLEMILK YOGURT

Calories	61
Protein	3.5 g
Fat	3.2 g
Carbohydrate	4.7 g
Vitamin A	30 mcg
Vitamin B5	0.4 mg
Vitamin B12	0.4 mcg
Calcium	121 mg
Iodine	35 mcg
Fluoride	12 mcg
Magnesium	12 mg
Phosphorous	95 mg
Potassium	155 mg
Zinc	0.6 mg

Frozen yogurt cups

MAKES 12

450 g/1 lb low-fat natural yogurt
1½ tbsp finely grated orange rind
225 g/8 oz mixed berries, such
  as blueberries, raspberries
  and strawberries, plus
  extra to decorate
fresh mint sprigs, to decorate
  (optional)

Method

1 Set the freezer to rapid freeze at least 2 hours before freezing this dish. Line a 12-hole bun tin with 12 paper cases, or use small ramekin dishes placed on a baking sheet.

2 Mix the yogurt and orange rind together in a large bowl. Cut any large strawberries into pieces so that they are the same size as the blueberries and raspberries.

3 Add the fruit to the yogurt then spoon into the paper cases or ramekins. Freeze for 2 hours, or until just frozen. Decorate with extra fruit and mint sprigs, if using, and serve. Remember to return the freezer to its original setting afterwards.

INDEX